WHAT ELSE IS THERE FOR A BOY LIKE ME?

Also by Patrick Moon

VIRGILE'S VINEYARD
A Year in the Languedoc Wine Country

ARRAZAT'S AUBERGINES
Inside a Languedoc Kitchen

To Jill and Wyndham

WHAT ELSE IS
THERE FOR
A BOY LIKE ME?

with much love

Patrick

PATRICK MOON

Matador
9 Priory Business Park,
Wistow Road, Kibworth Beauchamp,
Leicestershire. LE8 0RX
Tel: (+44) 116 279 2299
Fax: (+44) 116 279 2277
Email: books@troubador.co.uk
Web: www.troubador.co.uk/matador

ISBN 978-1783062-812

British Library Cataloguing in Publication Data.
A catalogue record for this book is available from the British Library.

Typeset in Aldine by Troubador Publishing Ltd, Leicester, UK

Matador is an imprint of Troubador Publishing Ltd
Printed and bound in the UK by TJ International, Padstow, Cornwall

Back cover image shows Mohamd (left) and author (right)

For Mohamd, of course

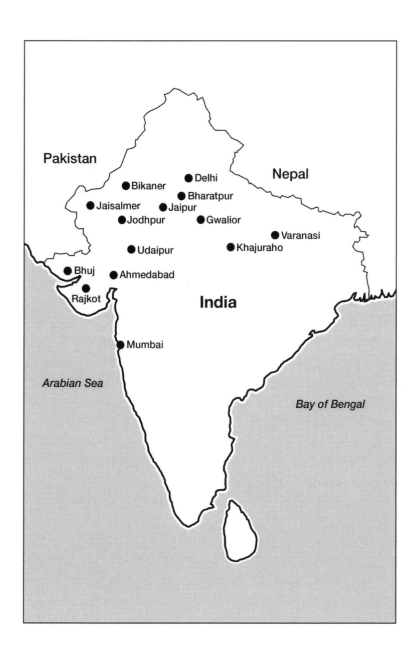

BEFORE

One

I wonder, am I the only passenger in this first class cabin who has abandoned his means of paying for such extravagances?

Until three weeks ago, I was a solicitor. I had been a solicitor for twenty years. And then I stopped. People keep telling me I'm 'brave' but, as Air India's senior hostess serves me caviar, I know that 'brave' is simply code for 'crazy'. The week when you've said goodbye to your income is hardly the moment for acquiring a taste for Sevruga. Glancing round the half-empty cabin, I count just seven fellow passengers: two indulging these gastronomic treats, the rest sleeping through them. I used to be part of all this, affording significant sums for trivial comforts. I was a well-rewarded partner in a large London law firm. Then I stopped. And now I feel guiltily out of place, a fraud, an imposter awake on a long journey.

'I knew you'd do this soon,' said my secretary, when I told her I was resigning. 'You've been a different person since you first went to India.' It wasn't that I hated my life as a lawyer. It would have been easier to do this if I'd seen it all as a mistake; but I didn't. I was good at it. I found it stimulating. Yet I didn't want to wake up one day, aged sixty, having done only one thing. So – I have to keep saying it to get used to the idea – I stopped.

That makes resigning sound like a snap decision – an impulsive, even whimsical severing from my past – but it wasn't. I hadn't stepped that far out of character. I'd been flirting with the idea for a few years but I needed more time to plan, more savings to cushion me. Then events made me act sooner than I intended.

'First time coming to India, sir?' asks a second sareed hostess, topping up my champagne.

'Third,' I boast, thinking how incredible that my first, just two years ago, was the only time I had ventured outside Europe. I came all this way for a week. With everyone saying I'd either love it or loathe it, I didn't want to waste too much treasured holiday finding out which. Yet I returned a lost cause.

The wrench of leaving India is no ordinary end-of-holiday sadness,' I wrote to my father at the end of that first visit. *'The rest of the world will no longer be the same, London miserably monochrome after the colours of Rajasthan... Yesterday we rose before dawn for an early flight, only to find the check-ins dark and deserted, thanks to a schedule change, which everyone except Mr Sharma, our guide, seemed to know about. "I am being very surprised," was all he could say. And how well that continuous present tense sums up these eight precious days. A state of constant amazement and wonder...'*

'You are coming for maybe three, four weeks?' asks the final member of the trio pampering the eight of us.

'Three or four months,' I correct her, wondering whether, if circumstances had been different, I'd have acted at all. I was too timid, too reluctant to let go, too afraid of casting aside my well-defined place in the world, too frightened of failure.

'So we are not seeing you again until... March, April?' she calculates, as if genuinely saddened by the wait.

'You won't see me at all,' I laugh ruefully. 'I'll be back there in economy.' I should be in economy now, but I persuaded myself I deserved a last luxury. That was part of my problem – working hard to pay for the treats that consoled me for working hard – a vicious spiral that I'll be glad to break. And yet I wonder how much economic simplification I shall really welcome. Or be able to live with.

'You are coming to Delhi for holidays?' my inquisitor persists, apparently determined to locate me in her scheme of things.

I smile as if to say 'yes' because how can I explain why I'm coming? I'm not even sure myself. Yet as soon as I knew that I could escape by the end of the year, there was never any doubt where I'd be spending my winter. I've never felt more compelled about anything in my life.

Even the business class passengers are held back behind a cordon of cabin staff while we, the select eight, make an unruffled exit. The others strain impatiently for release, tensing themselves for a hectic dash down the long, half-lit corridors. I myself am about to break into a sprint, remembering how the smallest delay could cost hours in the immigration queue. Yet tonight the passages are eerily empty, as if all human life has been banished to ease our unhurried progress.

Turning the corner, we find the hall of the passport control desks equally deserted – except, that is, for a single figure holding a signboard on a pole, as if he were stationed there to protest at our arrival. His handwritten text is a short list of names and I notice that one of them is mine. My seven companions show similar signs of recognition. Immediately, the demonstrator gives a blast on a whistle, confirming his opposition to our entry, while running footsteps suggest guards about to bar our way. However, the others know better. It is only the sound of eight breathless clerks, scurrying out from their tea break to open a dedicated counter for each of the favoured few and, in little more than a minute, I am standing beside eight sets of suitcases, set neatly apart from the chaos of the baggage carousels.

★

Of course, it's not just my relationship with India that I need to examine. There's also what my friend, Elektra, calls my relationship with myself. Elektra thinks this is the only issue, but then she's a psychotherapist. She thinks I *did* hate my life as a lawyer, when I wasn't busy hating myself. She says I need every minute of my time away, just to get twenty years of 'denial' out of my system.

I certainly need time to consider what comes next – a question that I'm trying to keep as open as possible. I need to put some distance between the past and the future. Too many old patterns of thought need purging before new ones can safely be let in. For the moment, there are just two things I'm sure about: one, I had to stop being a solicitor; the other, I had to return to India.

The airport is just as I remember: grey, grim and utterly unromantic but that doesn't stop an odd surge of emotion as I savour what, for me, will always be India's special smell. More evocative than the aromas of cumin and coriander from pavement kitchens or the stench of squalor in the gutter, it will be the smell of bed-linen through the coming weeks, the perfume of Indian laundries on shirts taken home to England. It is simply the comfortable, lived-in smell of warm dust. And it tells me: I'm back.

Most of my friends think I'll soon see sense – that, as soon as I've had my little spree, I'll simply tiptoe quietly back to the sane world of law; but I don't think I shall. There was a time when a few months' break might have done the trick, given other interests some temporary expression; but not now. I've changed. I've glimpsed freedom, caught sight of the possibility of doing something that matters to me. I want to spend the rest of my life thinking it's important, not just necessary, to get up in the mornings.

★

A bare-foot nine-year-old is tugging at my heaviest case, determined
to heave it onto a trolley, propelled by an even younger boy. 'Taxi,
taxi,' he jabbers, pointing to the waiting rank.

'No taxi.' I yank the trolley back and scan the waiting crowd
behind the barrier for a face that looks as if it might be scanning
the arrivals for me.

'This way, this way,' the boy insists, as my bags set off in the
opposite direction.

'Wait!' I protest, still searching for my name in the bobbing sea
of cardboard placards at the fence. 'Private driver this side…'

'Private driver?' queries the boy, as well he might. I've hired a
car, you see, and with it a driver. Elektra calls me 'the chauffeur-
driven drop-out' but how else would I get the freedom and
flexibility that I take for granted in Europe? I'm not sure whether
I'd be allowed to hire a car and drive it myself; but I've seen
enough of Indian roads to know it would be madness. In theory,
you drive on the left; in reality, you drive on whichever side is
emptiest, or over an adjoining field, if need be, so long as you fight
a route through the avalanche of oncoming traffic and animals. It's
not just quaintly chaotic, it's dangerous.

My first thought was to travel more 'authentically', with a
rucksack and a railway timetable – until I read a book that warned
me that I'd need to chain my bag to my ankle, if I ever thought of
sleeping on a train. Anyway, there was too much I wanted to bring,
to make the most of this opportunity, so for all these months the
boot of the car will be my storeroom and the car itself a kind of
home.

A home that will be shared, of course. My chosen means of
travel is going to bring me very close indeed to one slice of Indian
life. In all the weeks ahead, an unknown driver will be my daily

companion, the relationship far more 'real' than anything I'd be likely to find in station waiting rooms – indeed, close enough to make or break the whole journey. I'll have to do all I can to make it work.

'Mr Moon, sir! Mr Moon, sir!' calls an excited voice from the darkness at the back of the mob and, above the craning heads and waving arms, I glimpse a bright red logo, belonging to the company providing the car. Dragging both the trolley and the boys towards it, I find a short, plump figure in an undersized pullover teetering on tiptoe. 'Welcome again to Delhi,' says Adhvan Mahtani. At least that is what I think I think he says. His face is muffled against the night-time cold with a grubby scarf, looping round from his jaw to the top of his head, like a man with toothache. Pulling the mask aside for a second, he flashes me the manic smile that has welcomed me twice before. Then he shoos away the boys and gestures proudly towards the waiting vehicle.

It is, I am pleased to see, a classic off-white example of India's ubiquitous tourist motor, the 'Ambassador'. For as long as anyone can remember, these have been manufactured by Hindustan Motors, using time-warp, nineteen-fifties Morris Oxford machine tools. On my first visit, the name seemed to promise some sort of luxury limo, which the Ambassador was disappointingly not; but now I'd hate to hire anything else. They have always seemed indestructible. And what better vantage point than the broad, unusually high back seat for viewing all that there is to view?

Slumped against the driver's door is, I assume, my fate for the next few months: an elderly wraith with unconvincingly hennaed hair and a leather jacket several sizes too big for him. He is too preoccupied with rolling a cigarette to notice my arrival, until Mahtani barks something sharp in Hindi. Reluctantly, he hauls himself into an upright position and, pushing the cigarette behind his ear, shambles round towards the boot and my waiting luggage.

I put out my hand for an introductory shake but he takes no notice, merely sullenly manhandling my bags.

Mahtani senses quickly that I had hoped for better. 'Best in North India,' he promised, when I set all this up. 'Number One Guaranteed.' Well, if this is Number One...

'Sorry, sir,' he hastens to placate me. 'Driver only for Delhi, sir.' Mahtani's anxious breath makes clouds of steam in the crisp evening air. 'Khajuraho driver very good driver, sir. Specially picking.'

I'm flying to Varanasi tomorrow, then two days later on to Khajuraho; and only there, it seems, will I meet my long-term destiny, the much-vaunted Opie. (I've never in fact seen his name written down and have no idea how to spell it; but I'm Cornish and there was an eighteenth century Cornish portrait painter of that name, so 'Opie' will have to do.) If only I'd been able to book Krishan, from last year. I liked his driving; I liked his winning manner; and I so much wish I'd the security of those to look forward to for these many weeks, not this untried, unsettling Opie.

'Krishan lonely for wife in Kashmir,' says Mahtani. 'Leaving company, going back to her.' With a half-suppressed leer, he ushers me into the back and settles himself on the single wide seat in the front, beside the driver. Then he laughs disconcertingly. 'Opie very different fish kettle. Take it from me, sir...' More hearty laughter. 'There's only one Opie!'

I was also starting to feel that I'd achieved all I wanted to in the law. There was no unfinished business. I was close to the top of my field, with nowhere to go but down. And yet, I think I'd still be there, if it hadn't been for a sudden change of circumstances.

I'd been running a tight little specialist group. It wasn't what most people think of when they think about solicitors, nothing to make the headlines... We helped large public companies set up incentive schemes to motivate their employees, mostly through share ownership. So not exactly John Grisham. Anyway, there were three of us, just myself and two assistants, but very successful – until some competitors made spectacular pay offers to both young lawyers. I reckoned I could just about match these, but my partners were afraid of the domino effect on their own people, so I met with a veto. Yet I couldn't replace them. In three months I'd be on my own and I couldn't do the work of three people, nor be in three places at once. The only way to save both my sanity and my reputation was to add my own resignation to the heap, with no time for planning. I had to resign first and think later. Which is why I'm so unready, so unprepared for whatever lies ahead.

'So, third time coming to India?' Mahtani continues, as we lurch through the airport gates on to the busy dual carriageway. It is more of a statement than a question, as he personally masterminded both my previous journeys.

'Third time in Rajasthan,' I confirm. Mahtani knows that Rajasthan is where I intend to spend most of this winter and he must think me perversely unadventurous. With so much time at my disposal, I could tick off nearly every major sight in the country; but I am hoping that, by narrowing the focus, I'll penetrate some small distance beneath this country's unfathomable skin.

'But this time, no hotels in Rajasthan booking?' says Mahtani, plainly perturbed at the prospect of spontaneity.

My earlier visits were obsessively pre-planned, down to the finest detail. With every minute of permitted holiday a priceless resource, I was determined to eliminate the smallest risk of failure or frustration, regardless of cost. Then I had more money than time; now it's the other way round. Admittedly, I've pre-booked the first three hotels – in Delhi, Varanasi and Khajuraho – but only to fit round inflexible domestic flights. Half-ashamed, I've added a fourth, because Orchha seemed the only realistic stepping stone into Rajasthan; and, secretly, I think I know the next inevitable resting place, but I'm not admitting that to Mahtani.

'So, which places you go in Rajasthan?' he presses, still deeply troubled.

'No idea,' I tease him, then relent and offer a crumb: 'I do have to go to Jaisalmer.'

Mahtani scratches his head. 'Jaisalmer you visit last year, no?' He pauses, waiting for me to explain, but I hesitate. He'll never understand my reason for returning. 'Jaisalmer very beautiful,' he continues, as if to explain it to himself.

'I have to meet someone,' is all I volunteer.

Mahtani fidgets, clearly bursting with curiosity. 'Jaisalmer very long road,' he notes, hoping to draw me out, but I merely nod. It ought to be easy enough to explain: it was, after all, Mahtani's man in Jaisalmer who selected young Mohamd to be our guide there. So where's the harm in a satisfied customer renewing an old acquaintance? He ought to be delighted. Yet something tells me Mahtani simply wouldn't see the point of driving all that way for a penniless desert outcast.

'Is the boy worth it?' asked Elektra. 'Is he really so remarkable?'

'I've no idea,' I answered truthfully. 'I barely know him. But I've started something that I feel I have to finish.'

I only spent a day with Mohamd and I haven't seen him since, merely exchanged a few letters. I don't suppose he is – or ever will be – what Elektra judges 'remarkable'. But something about him touched me, made me pay more attention than I otherwise might have done. Maybe the innocent mix of ability and insecurity reminded me of myself at that age? Whatever it was, by the end of the day, this quiet, ordinary youth had convinced me that he had potential. He'd jolted me into sticking my neck out. I'd offered to help him. It seemed so simple and obvious: *I could change someone's life, just as India had changed mine.* Now I'm wondering what possessed me.

'How is family?' asks Mahtani, as if he knew and remembered them fondly. He has never betrayed any surprise that my wife and children should be left at home while I make these trips. He would have much greater difficulty in comprehending that they don't exist and never have. So, as usual, I treat his enquiry as referring to my father and sister.

'They're fine,' I tell him. 'And yours?'

'Oh, fine, sir. Still too many daughters,' he chuckles. 'But this time, your friend, sir, he is not coming to Rajasthan? This time coming alone?'

'It'll be good for me,' I tell him, wondering secretly whether I believe it.

'But later, sir…' Mahtani continues his probing. 'In Gujarat, your friend, same like first two times, he is coming?'

'Same like first two times,' I confirm.

'Do you think you'll still be the same?' asked Andrew, my partner for nearly twenty years. 'When you come back from India? You might find all these new, exciting parts of yourself and think me too boring!'

'I honestly don't know,' I told him reluctantly, as I packed my bags. I owed him better. Unselfishly, he had never once tried to talk me out of this, always backed me in what I felt I had to do; but I couldn't do glib reassurance very convincingly. 'I don't know who I'll turn out to be.'

'I'd better join you at half time to find out,' he answered with an anxious smile.

★

Andrew is the reason I consented to a week of fixed activity in Gujarat. That's because he's also a London solicitor... Did you notice that recidivist "also"? It may take me all of the winter to come to terms with the notion that I've actually put the law behind me... Anyway, when Andrew flies out to Ahmedabad, he'll come straight from a stressful office, needing efficiency and dependability, just as I used to.

'Your friend is hotels booking,' says Mahtani approvingly. 'Your friend is also *guide* booking.' Andrew is plainly Mahtani's kind of person. 'Mr Sharma, sir, guide on your first India tour, he was at airport tonight, meeting other Britishers. "Why Mr Moon not take guide?" he ask.'

'I am being very surprised,' I imagine him saying. We liked Mr Sharma. Sharma the Charmer we called him. However, this time, charm or no charm, I need to make my own way.

'So, three times making holiday with your friend,' observes Mahtani, plainly mystified. 'He, like you, coming always without family,' he adds with an admiring chuckle, as if he envied our success in shaking off these encumbrances. It simply hasn't occurred to him that the absence of Andrew's wife and children might be closely connected with the non-appearance of mine; however, this is not, I decide, the moment to shatter his worldview. In any event, he has now remembered some expectations that need to be managed. 'Delhi hotel you are choosing not five star, like last time,' he reminds me, as if to head off complaints in advance.

When I pressed for something modest, he grudgingly suggested The Residency, a sort of hostel, used mainly by senior armed forces personnel. I hardly thought about it at the time but, as I enter the bleak reception area, I am suddenly afraid it will be all regimental ties and moustaches, of which I have neither. I switch on the single-bar electric fire to take the chill off the room and set off in search of a restaurant.

Sooty smog is all around, as I pause on a deserted concrete bridge. Far below, some shadowy figures shiver round a feeble bonfire. A few dark shapes wrapped in blankets, hurry past me to somewhere warmer. The glow from the airport lights has completely disappeared and most of the stark urban landscape is now invisible. However, that doesn't stop me feeling very small in it.

'I still can't believe you're spending all these weeks in India,' said my father, calling from Cornwall to wish me safe travel.

'It's cheaper than running the central heating,' I joked, uncertain which bemused him more, my decision to leave the law or this sudden passion for a country that once made a different impression on a young conscripted sailor stepping ashore in 1940s Calcutta.

'I still can't forget the cripples,' he continued. 'And the poverty… the dirt…' I sensed a shudder, even down the telephone line.

'You get used to it,' I told him lamely.

His own career, running the pension scheme for the local County Council, had also been very different. Overworked until retirement, he had never felt in control of his own life and found it difficult to understand that I had used my control over mine to say 'no' to something enviable. He drew no comparisons, but still I felt a twinge of guilt. He had never known the luxury of this chance to change.

'What do you think did it?' he pressed me. 'I remember your letter – you said the rest of the world would no longer be the same, but I never really understood. What was it about India?'

'I wish I knew,' I confessed, although I wanted him to understand. Ever since my mother had died, six years previously, I seemed to need his approval more than ever. 'It was probably all subconscious… But how about this for a theory? Perhaps India corresponded to... or *encouraged* something... I don't know... something more irrational in me, something long-since hidden, *suppressed* even, but something that I was finally ready to unlock.'

'Have you been talking to Elektra?' He laughed at these unexpected words from such a high priest of order and reason.

'No, seriously,' I insisted, now excited by this glimmer of understanding. 'I think, in some strange way, it was India's spontaneity – all its colourful, chaotic diversity – that awakened something similar in me, made me less inhibited, less fearful of failure, more willing to let go...'

'I'm sure it'll all make sense by the end of this trip,' my father answered doubtfully.

No Indian hotel check-in would be complete without a detailed government registration form.

'*Coming from?*' asks the Varanasi receptionist, offering to complete it on my behalf. Answer: Delhi.

'*Going to?*' Answer: Khajuraho. I imagine some official, plotting my progress with coloured flags on a surveillance map.

'*Profession?*' This is more difficult. What can I answer but 'Solicitor'? After all, I still have the qualification, yet each affirmation of what I no longer am, or no longer *feel* I am, rings more hollow than the last – an almost daily reminder that I've discarded one identity, but have yet to find another.

I hadn't always planned to be a solicitor. As a child, I often dreamed of going into the theatre and I often ask myself why I didn't. I suppose, when it came to the point, I felt unready for the unpredictability of that world. A profession offered a structure, a system, a hierarchy. I could know my place, measure my progress. It was what I needed then.

'And now?' Elektra prompted.

'Now, I've a blank sheet of paper.'

'But what will you live on?' asked Alex, her husband, who makes a small fortune doing something I'd never quite understood in the city. I told him I'd saved a little during my final years in the law; that, if worse came to worst, I could manage without an income for maybe three or four years, but he wasn't reassured. 'That's your capital,' he protested. 'You can't spend your capital!'

'My real capital's my energy,' I insisted. 'The energy to attempt something new. I have to make sure I don't waste it.'

The hotel is big and impersonal but Varanasi didn't seem rich in alternatives. I considered taking my chance in the riverside guesthouses; but then I remembered that many would have come here to die. Varanasi being the *most* sacred of Hinduism's seven sacred cities, every devout Hindu is supposed to make at least one pilgrimage to wash away his sins in the holy waters of the Ganges, while anyone dying here is believed to go straight to heaven.

I linger with a snack by the pool. Remarkably, I've given no thought at all to my day. The old obsessive need to be planning seems finally to be waning. Yet, for all that, I feel guiltily conscious that I didn't come to Varanasi to sit in the sun.

But why have I come? Why this geographically anomalous bolt-on to an otherwise more focussed experience? An instinct perhaps that Varanasi was so important, so central to the country's spirit: it seemed a good place to start.

'Sorry for disturb.' A waiter pounces, as I put down my plate. 'Guide is in reception, sir.'

I was forgetting this. When I set things up, I told Mahtani firmly, 'No guides. Not even Mr Sharma.'

'Definitely, sir,' he said to me. 'But you do me one thing. In Varanasi you take guide.' And in the sheltered safety of another Ambassador, I start to see his point. Varanasi makes the bustle of

Rajasthan seem sedate. The pedal-rickshaws cycle four abreast, their bells ringing furiously. One carries what appear to be the total contents of the passenger's home, another a twelve-foot, vertical sheet of corrugated metal balanced on the customer's knees. Every vehicle in the city seems to klaxon, as we are slowed to a walking pace by a pair of small boys pushing a handcart, piled high above their heads with cottons. They are barely as tall as the Ambassador's bonnet and are nonchalantly oblivious to our bumper, nudging their little bottoms down the street. I feel overwhelmed by the sheer *quantity* of Varanasi.

Saving the river for tomorrow's sunrise, Amar, the guide, takes me to the Bharat Mata Temple – the only one in India without a single statue of a God or Goddess. In their place and carved in white marble, is a gigantic relief map of 'Mother India'. Amar points out Varanasi, then Khajuraho (he must have been talking to the receptionist), then my intended route through the Aravalli Mountains of Rajasthan. Near me in the north-west, close to the border with Pakistan, is the great Thar Desert, which I must cross to meet Mohamd; farther south the coastal state of Gujarat where I'll see Andrew; the whole of this the stage for whatever story the coming weeks are going to tell.

A second temple, the New Visvanath, is remarkable in a different way. Dedicated conventionally enough to Lord Shiva, its style is more eccentric: an opulent blend of grand hotel, 1930's cinema and a pink and white ice-cream sundae. Yet – exceptionally, Amar tells me – it is open to everyone, irrespective of caste. 'Even untouchables,' he emphasises, as the motley crowd sweeps us indiscriminately inwards.

'You are knowing about Hindu society?' asked Sharma the Charmer, within minutes of my feet touching Indian soil. 'How we are dividing into castes?' He was anxious to establish some essentials and the most essential of these was his own standing. 'I am being Brahmin,' he continued complacently. 'Brahmins highest caste: priests, sir. But I am not priest,' he added confusingly. I already knew about this complex social ordering, but I had also read about the struggle for democracy, about Gandhi's efforts on behalf of those lowest down the scale and, half a century on, I imagined most of these age-old distinctions would have dissipated their power. 'No, sir,' he disabused me, almost shocked at my naivety. 'Always Brahmins are marrying Brahmins, helping other Brahmins...'

'Giving jobs to other Brahmins?' I queried, wondering whether Mahtani boasted equal rank, but Mr Sharma had already returned to the pecking order.

'After Brahmins, are coming the Kshatriya: warrior persons, rulers...'

'Rulers after priests?' I interrupted, surprised.

He smiled his trademark smile to confirm his supremacy. 'In North, sir, these princes we are calling 'Rajputs'. Some are descending from Sun, through Lord Rama; others from Moon, through Lord Krishna.' He gave no sign of disbelieving any of this, merely commenting that they were mostly called Singh, meaning lion. 'Rajputs are having divine duty to fight,' he emphasised, citing various acts of credibility-straining bravery.

'And always Rajputs are marrying Rajputs?' I asked, inadvertently adopting the patois.

Mr Sharma beamed with satisfaction, before covering the two remaining tiers more briefly: the Vaisya, the merchants, followed by the Shudra or farming class. Then he hesitated, his smile a little more forced. 'These four castes are not including everyone, sir. Also, we have persons doing impure jobs... sweepers, leather tanners, these sorts of persons.'

'Untouchables?' I asked him bluntly.

'These days, mostly calling "Dalits",' he corrected me quickly. 'Sometimes calling "Scheduled Castes". But really, sir, these persons are not having caste.' He sounded oddly less comfortable with his superiority over society's outsiders.

'Surely nowadays, after Independence, after so much progress in education...'

'Oh, yes, sir. We are having much progress,' he confirmed, looking doubtful how good a thing this might be. 'Since 1947, all Scheduled Castes are having the positive discrimination – reserved seats in Parliament, one in three government jobs...'

'So a cleaner could marry a Brahmin?' I teased him, but he shook his head. 'You've not understood a thing,' his smile seemed to say.

I leave the hotel in darkness and drive through fog towards the Ganges. It is fiercely cold and thickly misty as we board our boat – an oarsman, Amar and I. Like everyone else, I buy a candle, circled with marigolds, and float it off down the river. 'You must send it with a prayer,' whispers Amar and I hesitate. I could, I suppose, ask for blessings for my journey. Or for Andrew. Or my father and sister. Perversely, sentimentally, I opt for a faraway desert boy that I met once and hardly know.

Washermen beat laundry on the steps leading down to the icy water. The more devoted of the pilgrims are braving the cold to bathe, while bonfires keep fainter hearts warm. Passing boats attempt to sell me trinkets but not even they can detract from an almost tangible sense of holiness. While Amar waits patiently, I immerse my thoughts in the sacred river, plunging gratefully deep below the dark surface, as far as imagination will take me from the profane world of employee benefits.

We leave the boat and walk a little nearer to the cremation sites. However, very few bodies are burning at this hour. Funeral parties, it seems, have more sense than tourists and are waiting for the morning sun.

'How was boat trip?' asks the driver, as if I were returning from a jolly seaside pleasure cruise. Unusually for Northern India, he has a crucifix and rosary dangling from his rear-view mirror and the burning grounds must be almost as remote from his world as they are from mine. He looks barely old enough to be allowed out unaccompanied, let alone to be driving. 'No, sir, I don't like this driving,' he answers my enquiry. 'But I have not another job.'

Well, I like his driving and I think I could like his company. I wonder whether I shall feel the same about Opie. This time tomorrow I'll know.

'I am following Lord Shiva,' Mr Sharma announced on that same first morning. He was keen to establish another fundamental and a giant Shiva statue near the airport provided his cue. 'Hindu Trinity: Brahma, Vishnu and Shiva, sir,' he continued. 'Some, they are following the Lord Vishnu; but mostly, they are not following the Lord Brahma.' As usual he made up in charm what he lacked in intelligibility. 'Brahma, he is Creator of Universe, Vishnu is Preserver, having ten incarnations – most famous, number seven the Lord Rama and number eight the Lord Krishna. Then Shiva, he is Destroyer.'

Creator, preserver, destroyer, I repeated to myself. Surely simple enough to see me through my temple visits.

'Lord Shiva is also Creator,' Mr Sharma added, confusing me again. 'Shiva's wife, Parvati, she is being also Kali and Shiva's son, Ganesh, having elephant head, very popular, God of good luck and prosperity. Also Hanuman, he is Monkey God and servant to Lord Rama...' The roll call continued for some minutes. 'You understand all this I am saying about Hindu Goddess and God?' he asked, when he finally ran out of steam.

'I'm not sure I could pass an exam on it,' I answered with reckless flippancy, only to hear him begin again: 'Hindu Trinity: Brahma, Vishnu and Shiva…'

Amar drops me off for breakfast and what he imagines will be a rest. However, my first unsupervised morning is too precious to waste. I want to explore on my own, but I scarcely reach the hotel steps before a crowd of children takes charge of me.

'Hello! Hello!' they all jabber. Then the litany, so familiar from my previous visits: 'What is your name, what is your country name, what is your job?' Except that, this time, I only know the answer to the first two questions. It seems that all Indians want to categorise, assign status, defining themselves, and determining their place in the world, by reference to everyone else. Like mariners with their sextants at sea, taking bearings from the stars to find out where they are, the Indian plots the position of others in the social landscape to find out *who* he is. How can I expect these children to understand that I've voluntarily surrendered twenty years of accumulated status, deliberately starting again from zero?

There is, in fact, a *second* standard conversation prescribed for encounters with children and my stroll this morning is no exception. 'One pen! One pen!' is how the other one goes. I packed a whole box of biros, but I keep forgetting to bring any out with me, so the supply is undiminished when it is time to meet Amar again.

He takes me back to the river to see what was earlier shrouded in mist. The most unexpected revelation is the fact that all of Varanasi stands on one side only of the Ganges. Even in the fog, I could see that we were clinging to the nearer bank but I assumed this was simply where the action was concentrated. I didn't realise that there was nothing on the other shore: nothing but bare, grey, featureless land, stretching away to the horizon. I can't think of any other city like it. The water has contained the town as decisively as if it were a precipice.

Most of the 'ghats' – the long, wide flights of steps leading down to the river – are less active in the afternoon sunlight than they were at dawn. Only the cremation ghat has a large crowd. The mood is infectiously reverential, despite the constant bustle of stretchers bearing new waves of bodies: some wrapped exquisitely in silks and garlanded with flowers; others roughly tied in grimy sheets and unadorned.

As we contemplate the burning pyres from the quiet of our boat, I learn that Amar is a proud product of Varanasi University – an English graduate, whose favourite author is, improbably, Thomas Hardy. Although he doesn't actually say that his college days were the best of his life, it seems to be written all over his sad, defeated face. He outlines a few vague strategies for more rewarding work, but I sense he has lost all his will to break out.

And suddenly it hits me like a punch in the stomach: an irrational dread that this is all I'll find in Jaisalmer – the same look of blank defeat on Mohamd's young face, the early spark of promise now extinguished, the energy to reinvent himself fizzled out.

'What else is there for a boy like me?' he once asked me.

Well, what else indeed?

What could I possibly have imagined?

Two

'My name is Rajput,' says the sharply-dressed leader of the two-man Khajuraho reception committee. Mahtani's local agent isn't just a *member* of the princely warrior caste. Rajput is actually the man's name and I can only assume that it was the burden of living up to this that drove him to cultivate his unashamedly preposterous moustache. 'Afternoon at leisure,' he notes, as he checks his dog-eared paperwork. 'Tomorrow and after tomorrow also at leisure,' he continues in tones of puzzled disapproval. 'Mostly guests staying two nights maximum, visiting temples only, but leave all to me, sir. I arrange.'

'There's really no need. I was thinking of a day in the countryside.'

'Exactly. I arrange jeep excursion.'

'Why would I hire a jeep? I'll have my own car.'

'Road is not good, sir.'

'The driver will have to manage. I can't afford both.'

At the mention of 'driver', Mr Rajput's acolyte springs forward. With a half-apologetic smile, as if excusing the lack of introduction, he starts bundling my luggage into a white Ambassador. I assume this is Opie but Rajput is too busy justifying the jeep to confirm or deny. The driver says nothing until we have dropped his superior at his office. Then he says a lot. He talks virtually non-stop and his single subject is my immense good fortune in securing his companionship for the coming months. As Mahtani said, there is only one Opie.

'You and me have very good time,' he promises, with a pat on the head for the plastic, elephant-headed figure, looking pleased with itself on his dashboard. According to Mr Sharma, this will be Ganesh, the God of prosperity, which probably tells me all I need to know about Opie's idea of a 'good time'. He's less immediately engaging than Krishan, but speaks better English and looks very professional in his light grey trousers and matching shirt with button-down epaulettes. He's very affable too. In fact, behind his curly beard, he grins and laughs a great deal. I just wish he wouldn't swing all the way round to look at me when he does so; or if he must take his eyes off the road, at least drive a little less aggressively. Also, there's something about the smile that faintly bothers me. Perhaps it's merely bad dentistry that gives it the occasional cruel twist.

'First to temples?' he asks cheerfully and I hesitate. The temples are, after all, why I'm here. They're the reason why this small, unremarkable town has its airport. Elektra gave me a lavishly illustrated book on the subject: *Khajuraho, An Introduction to the Erotic Temples*, no doubt trusting in the ruder illustrations to help me shed some inhibitions! It persuaded me that anywhere worth a whole book had to be worth a visit, even a further deferral of my return to Rajasthan. Tonight, however, a crowded market sparks a better idea and Opie obligingly performs an emergency stop, laughing loudly at the tooting of a lorry stuck behind us, while I find what I need in the boot.

The video camera was a leaving present from a favourite client, one of the few that I felt genuinely close to. When I started my lawyer's life, there seemed to be time to know more about the clients than the minimum that their problems required me to be told. They even spared a moment to know something about me. A human context underpinned the business one. Soon, however, 'time recording' changed all that, as life came to be divided up into six-minute units, each with an exorbitant price tag. It must be difficult for anyone whose life has never been ruled in this way to understand the contaminating effect of the pressure to record and then sell every second. It took a long time for me to see it myself. Then I found myself in supermarket queues, muttering, 'Don't these people realise how expensive my time is? The wait's costing more than the groceries!' That's when I knew it was time to stop. And where better now to change the rhythm of my life than India – timeless, unpunctual, unflustered India?

I wave apologetically to the impatient truck driver and set about filming the market. It was the colours that attracted me: the oranges and yellows of the marigolds piled in baskets, waiting to be threaded onto temple garlands; the ochres, reds and browns of the bulging spice sacks. Soon, however, people take priority. Chirpy children, clamouring for stardom, push their way forward. 'One photo, one photo,' they chorus, unaware that this is a movie shoot.

My client has even spoiled me with the latest technology. No doubt, one day these digital cameras will be commonplace but, for the moment, they are state of the art. Certainly, no one in the Khajuraho market has ever seen one.

'What is your name?' I ask each child, as they solemnly recite their answers. Flipping the monitor screen, I press the play-back button and they explode with uncontrollable delight. Then Opie shoos them roughly aside.

Armed with Elektra's book, I have waved aside the would-be escorts at the western group of temples. It's the profusion of figure carvings for which these are famous, the erotic ten per cent the most famous of all, and I learn from the book that we owe these to Tantrism, a minority Hindu cult that sees the gratification of sensual desire as a step towards spiritual enlightenment. I also learn that Hinduism isn't so much the worship of many gods of bewildering variety, rather a belief that the Divine can be manifested in countless different forms, pervading the whole of the universe, the whole of life. Which is why it's such a *way of life*. Also why the sacred and the profane – to the West, so separate – are here so intertwined, or more accurately one.

Oblivious to such insights, my driver is waiting in the car. That is to say, he is sleeping in the car, snoring heavily, with his knobbly stockinged feet poking out through one of the windows. There are yellow sweat stains on the soles of his pale grey socks but at least they are outside the window.

Jumping back to life, he says he remembers me from my second visit to Rajasthan. We overlapped, it seems, in the small town of Deogarh, when he was there with some other Mahtani customers. I'm surprised I don't remember. I usually have a good memory for faces. But perhaps he didn't have his beard. Wisely probably. From certain angles, it makes him look sinister.

The last of my last-minute purchases was a neat little 'palmtop' computer. 'First the limousine, now the cyber connection!' mocked Elektra, keen as ever to lumber me with her asceticism, but it wasn't my intention to cut myself off (much as she might think it good for the self-analysis). 'They do have telephones in India,' she reminded me, but I tried to explain: I could send off emails whenever I had access to a telephone line, without having to worry what time it was at the other end; and friends could reply when it suited them, without needing to know where I was. 'Hmmph,' was all she replied.

There have been telephone lines in my hotel rooms, but Elektra will be glad to know that I've drawn the line at such profligacy. Instead, I use my Khajuraho lunch-break to seek out one of India's Private Call Offices – a 'PCO', as the country's penchant for abbreviations prefers it, offering two famous, world-beating services: Subscriber Trunk Dialling, better known as STD, and International Subscriber Dialling (ISD). They usually consist of just a minuscule shop, housing a desk, a chair and a telephone connected to a government-approved meter, which times the call and calculates the charge. In this case, the regulation yellow sign, bearing the vital letters 'PCO-STD-ISD', hangs in front of someone's living room.

The resident family interrupts its meal and squeezes to one side. I show the father of the house my palmtop, miming the plugging-in of the modem wire, but he clearly knows nothing of such things. 'STD? ISD?' he prompts, having only these two products on offer. If neither of these is of interest, his wife and children might reasonably return to their food.

'ISD,' I confirm. 'But no speaking, only computer.'

Without understanding, he allows me to connect the lead but the palmtop fails to dial. As the lunch congeals, I try everything I can think of, until the battery runs out. I offer him something for his time, but he points to the zero on the meter. 'Tomorrow come back,' he proposes, surely masochistic beyond the call of duty. My expensive toy was a waste of money that I can ill afford.

The eastern and southern groups of temples seem less impressive; or is it just that I'm distracted by a pair of village lads that refuses to be shaken off? 'Not for guiding,' they insist, trailing me from bas relief to bas relief. 'Only company keeping. English practising...' They do, however, confess to a shop, wondering whether I might, if time permits, and if nothing more pressing has a prior claim on my attention, possibly visit the same.

'Maybe later,' I prevaricate, as they shadow me to the next façade.

'Sir, you promise,' they beseech me, at the end of a long afternoon. 'Very good lucky,' they add, as they hustle me into a small stone shed to view a tawdry collection of metal Ganeshes. 'How many you like?'

Unfortunately, I saw some antique (well, oldish) pieces in another shop on the way to the PCO, so I tell the boys 'none' and immediately they demand to be rewarded for their guiding services. Having no small notes, I give to one of them considerably more than they deserve for division between them; but I can see that he has no more intention of sharing than I have of duplicating the largesse.

'You look now in this my friend's shop,' says Opie, steering me towards a second shed. The 'friend' looks oddly like an older version of Opie – complete with curly beard and crooked teeth – yet I suspect they've only known each other for about as long as I spent in the first establishment. Not that this inhibits Opie from joining in the sales effort. I insist on returning to my earlier discovery, where I try to negotiate a discount; however, the vendor is firm: no discounts, no drivers' commissions, hence keen prices.

'No problem,' says Opie, but there is something falsely bright about his enquiry after my plans for tomorrow.

'Rajgarh,' I tell him.

'I know,' says Opie, yet somehow I sense that he doesn't.

Rajgarh is a relatively minor Rajput palace, in a poor state of repair and likely to be little visited. I know this because Andrew, not to be outdone by Elektra, gave me a book by a Cambridge don, covering most of the ones in Northern India. Opie runs an index finger slowly along the title: *The... Rajput... Palaces... The... Develop... ment... of... an... Architect... ural... Style... 1450-... 1750... by... G... H... R... Tillot... son.* He glances quickly at Mr Tillotson's Rajgarh section, all grainy black and white photographs and dense, academic text. He is unenthused. 'You make more movie?' he asks, uncomprehending.

'I might make a painting,' I tell him to add to his bafflement.

★

'You won't be able to afford your expensive pictures,' said Alex, trying to talk some sense into me, when he heard of my resignation. 'No more Saturday impulse buys.' My regular companion in the art galleries, he was going to miss all the fights over who saw the best canvas first.

'I'd rather have the time to paint my own,' I answered defiantly.

'You never told me you painted!' He sounded more shocked than surprised, as if at some betrayal.

'I don't. I haven't had time since I was a lawyer, but I used to. As a boy, I was seldom very far from a sketchbook, but now... I don't know when I last tried. I want to see if I still can.'

So I made some more last minute purchases – not just paints, brushes and paper, but a collapsible easel and a stool that folded up into a sort of rucksack. 'Is it just the one car you're hiring?' laughed Alex.

Opie latches on cheerfully to the concept of driving me out to dinner. 'If you are happy, I am happy,' he says: a philosophy at which I can hardly complain. 'I know all the places,' he assures me and we look at three or four of his favourites, a sample large enough to demonstrate the man's almost unswerving passion for plastic – in the furniture, in the tablecloths, even the curtains. Only the last, with its tables made of concrete, breaks the pattern.

'You like beer?' asks Opie. 'First we buy beer, sir. Then you take to restaurant.' We stop at a heavily barred liquor store and I offer him one for himself, which he graciously accepts, but the 'guards', seeing my western face, propose a price that he considers outrageous, so we leave again, beerless. Then, halfway to the concrete tables, he spots a pedestrian who works for Mr Rajput and we all drive back again, securing three bottles at a price that they both find acceptable.

At the restaurant door, Opie hides the bottle for me in his deep trouser pocket. 'No beer permit,' he explains and, after much negotiation with the manager, my beer is discreetly decanted into a teapot and served in a cup and a saucer. 'How you like your special tea?' ask the waiters, in fits of giggles, apparently determined to draw maximum attention to my cunningly disguised refreshment.

Opie returns periodically to check that I'm happy. He seems pleased that I'm amused by the subterfuge and our 'secret' binds us together. Then, at the end of the evening, he insists on negotiating a discount on my bill and I'm not sure whether this is funny or embarrassing. I like the feeling that he's on my side but, while he disappears (I suspect) to claim his commission, I leave the discount on the plate as a tip. That is *my* secret.

The lights of the Private Call Office are still lit – the long-suffering household now gathered round the television – and I decide to call Andrew. It's the first call I've made since I left but, with hardly a moment for preliminaries, I launch straight into my internet problem, asking him to contact my email provider. The answer is drowned by the television; then my host obligingly turns the volume down and Andrew tells me once again, this time impatiently, that he doesn't see the point. 'Is this really what you're calling for?' he asks pointedly, but I'm too preoccupied to take the hint.

'There may be some different software,' I urge him, clutching at straws. 'You could bring it out to Gujarat.'

'What about Jaisalmer?' he changes the subject. 'Have you rung Mohamd?'

'Not yet. There's no hurry. I don't think I'll get there before Gujarat.'

'You ought to check that he'll be there. You don't want to drive all that way to find he's gone off somewhere.'

'Where could a boy like him go?'
'I still think you should ring.'

'Muslim name, Hindu boy,' Mohamd was quick to explain. He was only eighteen but, with his earnest frown and solemn civility, he might have passed for older. The neatly cut, lightly oiled hair looked especially plausible. Only the scuffed lace-up shoes and the boyish striped T-shirt, beneath a more business-like black anorak, gave him away.

He took us first to Gadi Sagar, the beautiful natural lake outside the city, then to the magnificent City Palace and finally to the merchants' houses, the so-called *havelis*, where we climbed to a rooftop to see the city in perspective. And it was here, dropping the polite professional mask, that he made a small, shy confession: he often went there to look at girls on other rooftops. One in particular, about a hundred yards away, seemed to half-wave in our direction, then modestly turned away.

'Your girlfriend?' Andrew teased him.

'No,' Mohamd laughed, embarrassed.

'Your fiancée, then?'

He laughed again, blushing beneath his dark olive skin. 'In my community, the parents decide these things.' It was the first time I'd properly looked at him, considered what kind of person might be hiding there behind the formal courtesies. 'Tell us about your community,' I prompted, remembering Mr Sharma's social hierarchy.

'My family name is Nayak,' said Mohamd. 'We are like small Rajputs. In history, we fought beside Rajput kings, but not so powerful.' Removing his jacket in the sunshine, he looked skinnier, more child-like, not at all in the warrior mould. Then with a bashful grin, he pointed to one of the earrings that he wore in each ear – a circular brass disc, set with red and white enamel. 'Also traditional in my community,' he explained. 'But not expensive,' he added swiftly, in case we got the wrong idea. Then the mask fell back into place and we continued our tour.

Towards the end of the morning, Mohamd asked attentively, 'You feeling maybe little bit tired? My friend living just down this street. We can take tea.'

Riyaz, the friend, lived in a shop called Cottage Gallery. He was from Kashmir, like his tea; and, as Andrew and I sipped the delicious, spiced brew, he filled the carpet in front of us with Kashmiri handicrafts. 'I Tell You Honestly, Sir…' Riyaz had a unique way of speaking that somehow emphasised every word. 'I Tell You Honestly, Sir. This Best Quality. You Try Other Shop In Jaisalmer, You Not Find Like This.'

Mohamd discreetly withdrew to the street. He probably never expected us to buy so much. Friends at home were equally surprised. Yet I *needed* these things: they had to sustain me until I could come back.

Leaving Mohamd at the shop, Krishan, the driver, ferried us back to the hotel outside the city, promising to return again at two-thirty with our guide. This, he insisted against our protests, was the latest time we could leave for our camel safari in the sand dunes. So reluctantly, at the prescribed hour, we tore ourselves away from the swimming pool, only to find Krishan and the car, but no Mohamd. We were not pleased. We waited for twenty-five minutes (more than four of those six-minute 'time sheet units') and we paced and we grumbled, arguing between ourselves whether all or only part of his tip should be forfeit. Andrew was more forgiving. Finally, we saw a three-wheeler auto-rickshaw turning in through the hotel gates.

'I was posting some greetings cards,' Mohamd apologised, as if this might make things all right. Then he saw that it didn't. He sat cowed in the front seat, unable to understand – let alone *melt* – the wall of frost that divided him from the back. There was little perceptible thaw, by the time that we climbed into our saddles and set off alone with the camel driver. However, ice couldn't survive long in the desert sun – or even in the gentle, restorative warmth of Mohamd's company, when he met us at the other end. He came running towards us from a distant ridge, waiving cheerfully as he scampered barefoot over the sand, his lace-ups in one hand and some refreshing bottled water in the other. As we sat to watch the sunset, he told us a little of his life... the life of a plucky, shy, resilient, vulnerable boy who could only be forgiven.

We should already have left for Rajgarh, but Opie says I have to see Mr Rajput and Mr Rajput says I have to take a guide. Having failed to sell me the jeep, he now wants to sell me the shambling, lacklustre youth at his side. I say that I can manage with my driver, but Mr Rajput begs to differ: Opie doesn't know the way. 'Surely he can ask,' I protest, while Opie says nothing. In the end, I acquiesce but it soon becomes clear that the boy knows little more than either of us. We keep stopping for directions from passing shepherds and unfortunately – I have noticed this before – there are two inflexible rules operated by Indians giving directions. First, they will never admit their ignorance of the place you are trying to find, offering full, yet entirely fantasised advice on how to get there. Second, each set of instructions will directly contradict those most recently received. In two hours of driving, I sense that we are never far from Khajuraho.

The team now insists that lunch must be organised before the palace and finding lunch proves as difficult as finding Rajgarh. After many wrong turns, we reach a farmhouse. 'NO ADMITION WITHAUT PERMITION,' says an unpromising sign, but Opie drives in regardless, proclaiming our desire to take lunch on the farmer's lawn – a suggestion which, amazingly, is welcomed.

As the three of us wait awkwardly in the sun, the conversation is stilted. Away from the usual script, my driver's English proves limited and, as for the boy, it takes him three attempts to make me understand that his ambition in life is to be an English-speaking guide. I don't have the heart to ask if he has considered alternatives.

'You like beer, sir?' asks Opie, filling one of the silences, and I offer to share a big bottle of Kingfisher, sipping mine slowly, while he drains his. 'You like more beer?'

'No, thank you, I'm fine.' The level in my own glass has hardly moved and I try to inch open a book without seeming aloof.

'I drink mostly wine,' I volunteer to fill another silence.

'This Indian wine not good.' Opie gives the fastidious wince of a connoisseur. 'All are these tourists not liking. All are these tourists liking beer.' He looks meaningfully at my glass, hoping to drain it through the power of suggestion. Then another line of enquiry occurs to him: 'You drink whisky, sir?'

'Sometimes. Only in the evenings, but yes, I bought some malt at the airport...'

Opie grins approvingly. He clearly likes whisky a lot – nearly as much as he likes beer – and it occurs to me, there was a driver in Deogarh who took Krishan off for a drunken barbecue, causing a murmur of displeasure from the hotel. I'll bet that was Opie. But so long as he does his drinking at night and is unimpaired by day, why should I worry?

Mohamd's family lived in a small desert village. At the age of eleven, he had taken himself off to the city, enrolling in a school and earning just enough on the fringes of the tourist industry to support himself. Most of what he knew about Jaisalmer had been learnt by listening to other guides. Most of his English had been picked up from tourists. Likewise his competent French, Italian and Spanish, not to mention basic Japanese. And he was only eighteen. Surely, I thought, someone with this much ability and initiative could go further, if he could only break free, before defeat overwhelmed him, like so many others.

'Have you thought what else you might like to do?' I asked, as we sat in the sand dunes. 'You can't just trail around the City Palace for the rest of your life.'

'What else is there for a boy like me?' he answered philosophically.

'You're good with people,' prompted Andrew. 'You might make a hotel manager.'

'For that I'd have to go to Delhi. I can't afford the bus fare, never mind the study fees. And it costs four times as much to live in Delhi.'

'You could have a shop, like Riyaz.'

'For that I'd need big sum of money to start.'

Everything seemed to run into the same financial block. There was nothing new in his predicament. I'd seen it often enough in India, this combination of wide promise and narrow prospects. Mohamd was just lucky. He hit a point in my life where I felt his country had given me so much that I wanted to put something back. I knew I could never make any impact on the big problems – probably nobody could – but maybe I could help solve a small one. The sort of money that I'd spend casually on a picture might transform just one individual's life. I felt I had to try.

Neither of us said any of this to Mohamd. Indeed, Andrew didn't even know that I was thinking on these lines. We simply gave him many times the usual tip and praised him to the sky in his appraisal form – except for one thing: I complained about the lateness. 'He has to learn,' I persuaded the more merciful Andrew.

As he left us, Mohamd scribbled the address of Riyaz's shop on a scrap of paper. 'You can write to me,' he said hopefully.

'Where you stay in this Orchha?' asks Opie, driving slower than usual through the dense morning fog.

'The Sheesh Mahal,' I tell him, looking up from my reading.

'Part of the Royal Palace.' The full complex merits seventeen pages in the Tillotson tome and, as 'Sheesh Mahal' means 'Mirror Palace', I'm already picturing myself in some magnificent, mirrored bed chamber.

'Government hotel,' says Opie gruffly, as if this were all the condemnation needed. 'I show you better place.'

'But I've already paid. I've got a voucher...'

'I show you better place,' he says again.

The fog refuses to lift but Opie's driving feels reassuringly safe. The back seat, stocked with books, CDs and a portable player, feels equally reassuringly like home. The whole car smells pleasantly of incense, thanks to a joss-stick smouldering gently beneath the plastic Ganesh: Opie's offering for prosperity, I assume. For some reason, the upholstery is all wrapped in fitted covers, made of pale blue towelling and I've been imagining Mrs Opie (if there is a Mrs Opie) stitching these lovingly in the long dull evenings while her husband is away. However, the covers already seem subtly greyer than when we started; and Opie's formerly spruce, light grey trousers and matching shirt look more mottled and crumpled. He must be economising and sleeping in the car. Hence, of course, the joss-stick air freshener.

Opie is very much in talkative mode, turning swiftly to the subject of Krishan. Mahtani was tactless enough to tell him how hard I pressed to have Krishan as my driver and this is clearly sensitive territory. It prompts a further run-down of Opie's unique selling points: his unrivalled skills at the wheel, his unprecedented knowledge of the terrain and, most important of all, his total lack of interest in the sordid world of commission payments so dear to most of his profession: in short, a paragon among drivers. However, the talk of commission – to which, he reminds me, he's indifferent – quickly sparks a searching enquiry into the nature and extent of my shopping plans.

I tell him I don't really have any. Then I admit that I might look for a marble tabletop in Agra, perhaps a carpet from a man near Jodhpur, but none of the usual tourist shopping. I'm trying to establish some ground rules, preparing him for the fact that I may be a bit of a disappointment. 'I show you better places,' is his only comment.

'Won't he think it strange?' said Andrew. 'Getting a letter like this from a tourist he only met for a day?'

'That's why it's better that it comes from both of us.'

'He'll still think it strange.'

'He can think what he likes. We have to make the offer.'

So I wrote to Mohamd. I told him of our willingness to help. It was for him to decide what he wanted to do. We weren't trying to steer him. But if we could help him get his foot on a ladder of his choosing, he should write to us.

It was several months before he replied. We thought our letter must have gone astray. Most young men would have answered by return, suggesting plenty of ways of spending the undisclosed sum on offer, but we checked through Mahtani's man in Jaisalmer and, yes, the young Mr Nayak had indeed received our mail, yet still there was no reply. We must have hit the wrong note, offended his 'minor Rajput' pride in some way. We should never have stuck our necks out. Andrew told me he had told me so.

Then a letter arrived, written on a sheet of paper from an exercise book. He apologised for the delay. He apologised for writing an ordinary letter, not a computer letter. And he thanked us for our offer. But he was fine for the moment. He wanted to finish his studies:

'I have exams beginning next month, so I left gideing for two months. I hope I can be secusful in my exams. After exam I see what to. I don't no yet. I wright you two litters every

37

month. You don't need to wright two litters to me. You can
wright me just one litter. Again sorry for late...'
It seemed he needed to get used to us as pen friends, before he
could cope with us as benefactors.

'Orchha many kilometre far,' grumbles Opie, as I set up my
painting stool in a teeming but nondescript village on the highway.
    We never in fact made it to Rajgarh. Or rather, it had closed by
the time that we found it. So I never had a chance to try my paints
and now I'm determined to have a go, seething hubbub or no
seething hubbub. But, unfortunately, I'd forgotten how difficult
watercolours are, especially for one who has barely lifted a brush
in twenty years: you can't paint over your mistakes and, jostled
from every side by the crowd, I make plenty of those. To Opie's
relief, I'm soon tearing the picture up.
    The quality of the road gets steadily worse. We pass numerous
broken-axled, overturned lorries, their top-heavy loads strewn
chaotically over the pot-holed surface. The oncoming traffic weaves
an unpredictable slalom course through the mayhem, waiting till
the last possible second for avoiding action. 'Horn Please' says the
legend on each of the gaudily painted trucks crawling ahead of us –
a request that anyone overtaking should politely advertise the fact
or, in Opie's case, an injunction to keep his hand on the hooter for
as long as there is another vehicle in sight. Yet, for all this, there is
something therapeutic about driving (or at least being driven) in
India. The limited engine power, the state of the roads and the
volume of 'opposition' make for average speeds around thirty miles
per hour. The sheer inevitability of the gentle pace makes it
unexpectedly relaxing. Only weeks ago, I'd have been seething
with impatience. Now, I positively relish this sense of time
stretching.
    I load a CD to pass the time, but none of my carefully selected

'Desert Island Discs' fits the rhythm of the road and, in any case, my driver is still intent on conversation. He presses to learn more about my plans, as keen to learn precisely what lies ahead as I am to resist such precision. With Orchha my last reservation before Gujarat, I'll soon be free, but Opie is bursting with suggestions, foremost among them a place called Dariawad. 'All are these tourists liking. Famous for flying squirrel...'

'Flying *squirrel?*' I laugh, thinking he's making this up, but he insists.

'No, sir, really. We go there after Gujarat.'

'I have to meet a friend in Jaisalmer after Gujarat.'

Opie talks of other things, while he worries away at this intriguing piece of information; then, unable to contain himself, he returns to the topic. 'This friend in Jaisalmer... This is local person?'

'Local person, yes.'

'Is lady person?' he asks, with a wink and a smirk.

'Not a lady person,' I tell him unhelpfully and he frets for a few minutes more.

'Is working in some tourist activity?' he asks at last and I decide that I have tortured him enough. I admit that Mohamd was my guide, then quickly emphasise that he has since become my friend. Yet, even as I say this, I know it's absurd to call him that. He's an abstract, a symbol of his country, a convenient conduit for a charitable impulse. I'm returning to Jaisalmer to give some impetus and direction to these wheels that I've rashly set in motion, but it's starting to feel like more of a duty than a pleasure. If only I'd kept to conventional philanthropy. So much easier in the old days, sending cheques from the lazy safety of my office to remote, impersonal charities. What I've started here needs *work!*

Opie's Orchha hotel is immaculate, filled with rich fabrics, gleaming polished wood, elegant marble... and the welcoming smile of the receptionist is as bright as the badge on his lapel, reading 'Sanjay'. 'Now to Sheesh Mahal,' says Opie smugly.

Although the principal palaces were abandoned in the eighteenth century, the trusty Tillotson assured me that the Sheesh Mahal remained in use until Independence. Well, today it looks nearly as neglected as the rest and I look in vain for the glittering mirrors of my imaginings. Behind the crudely carpentered reception desk is a surly-looking figure, surely well past retirement age, slumped peacefully over a newspaper. Yawning, he rises slowly to his feet, only mildly curious as to why I've intruded, and shambles ahead of me down an unlit corridor to what he assures me is his best room. A glance at the shabby interior makes my mind up: I'm going back to Sanjay.

'Refund not possible,' says the elderly drudge, more puzzled than annoyed.

'No problem,' says Opie. 'I telephone my office, Mahtani explaining, voucher changing, many times I am doing.' But Mr Fixit fails to fix this one. His call, on Sanjay's telephone, produces no joy. Well, so be it. I'll spend my way out of a miserable night.

'You stay one night or two?' asks Opie, before Sanjay can ask me himself.

'Only one...' I begin.

'Only one,' repeats Opie, as if Sanjay might not have heard.

'Tomorrow I thought maybe Datia.'

'No good hotel. Better second night here.'

'I'll just see the palace in Datia, then drive on.'

'Which place you stay?' demands Opie, in a tone that says 'Where could be better than here?'

Where indeed? But Rajasthan is exercising its strange, strong pull, and I'm determined to get to Gwalior, putting me well on the way to the border. 'I'll decide in the morning,' I lie, hoping to leave him in suspense.

'Gwalior good place,' he suggests.

I'll need to try harder, if I want to keep him guessing.

My friend Tillotson gets particularly excited about the fact that Datia's Palace lacks a separate ladies' section – a *zenana*, as Mr Sharma taught me to call them. 'Maharajas having many wives,' I remember him saying. 'Living all the time in the purdah.' In Urdu, he explained, 'purdah' meant a curtain, behind which a woman of high status had to be hidden. Indeed, many Rajput princesses were forbidden ever to leave their *zenanas*, seeing only children and other women. He showed me the intricately carved screens – the so-called *jali* windows – through which the royal ladies kept their avid watch on the outside world. 'But not any more,' insisted Sharma, the modern man. 'All is history now. Maharanis, they are driving motor cars.'

Yet I wonder. In sophisticated aristocratic circles, perhaps. At a humbler level, it's always the young men who look after me in the hotels, small boys who pester me in the streets. Their sisters are altogether less visible. True, there are women aplenty at the roadside, balancing water pots and firewood on their heads. It's even the women who *build* the roads, carrying baskets of stone and digging trenches, while a token male sits on his haunches to supervise. Yet they all veil their faces, before there's any danger of my catching their eye.

'Finished?' asked Opie, impatient to put Datia behind him.

He could scarcely believe my two hours in the palace, still less the time I wanted to waste painting a greengrocer's stall; but I had settled in for the remainder of the morning, so he settled more or less patiently on a nearby step. From time to time, he broke the monotony with a spot of crowd control, hurling Hindi invective at the art lovers pressing round me. Occasionally, the stallholder hobbled over to check that I was doing his emporium justice. He seemed content and so was I. I felt I was improving.

'Which place in this Gwalior?' asks Opie, as soon as I return to the car.

'I thought I'd look around...' I try to sound vague, but the books all agree: there's only one salubrious option, the Usha Kiran Palace, once a guesthouse for the Maharaja's European visitors.

'Usha Kiran good place,' he announces, so at least we agree on something. 'All are these tourists liking,' he adds, making me fearful that they might not have a room; then, with barely a pause: 'Which place after?'

'I haven't decided.' The Bharatpur bird sanctuary seems a near certainty but I'm not letting on.

'Bharatpur good place,' he says cheerfully. 'But only one good hotel, Laxmi Vilas, very small.' Another twinge of fear as to vacancies. 'Then no more booking before Gujarat?' He shakes his head, as if he shares the fear.

'Exactly,' I almost snap. The man spends too much time with Mahtani.

'Last night in Delhi booking,' he observes, as if he has just caught me out. 'Same hotel, Residency, going back.'

'I needed somewhere close to the airport...'

'Night before, in Neemrana booking,' he persists, almost jubilantly.

'There were special reasons...'

'My village only twelve kilometre far from this Neemrana,' he interrupts, then turns abruptly quiet, leaving the thought of this proximity dangling portentously in a long silence.

'I was wondering about lunch,' I venture after a while.

'No good place on this road.' Opie's tone says, he did try to get me to Gwalior by lunchtime. Then a thought strikes him: 'You like very typical restaurant?' Without waiting for an answer, he pulls off the road beside a corrugated metal shack. Under the shade of a plastic tarpaulin, a cook and his customers are sleeping off their food on some wooden-framed string beds. 'Bed name *charpai*,' says Opie, brushing dust from one of these for me to sit on. '*Char* mean four, *pai* mean leg...' The language lesson is apparently intended to put me at my ease. 'Food here very clean,' he adds, rousing the chef with a kick to the neighbouring bed. 'You like veg or non-veg?' he calls, as he crosses to the blackened cooking pots. There was only 'veg' at the Khajuraho farm, so the question didn't arise.

'Vegetarian,' I tell him firmly, although there's nothing doctrinal in this, just a sense of caution born of open-air butcheries seen in Indian markets.

'You like only veg or sometimes non-veg?' he asks, having bustled round attentively to find a teaspoon for my watery yellow curry.

'Almost only veg,' I answer, but the question is no mere lunchtime small talk. Opie's mind is still on my night at the Neemrana Fort, the luxurious extravagance that I've promised myself before the last drive to Delhi.

'You come to this my village,' he proposes, kneading chapatis into his own plate of gruel to make a slushy paste, which he raises to his lips in dripping fistfuls, while I manage mine as if it were soup and bread. 'All are these tourists meeting my wife, eating dinner,' he continues, slurping noisily. 'She is very happy. Veg, non-veg, no problem. She cook very good meat...'

'We'll have to see,' I play for time, but Opie has already moved on.

'This Jaisalmer person...' he asks, as we return to the car. 'He is young person, sir?' The scandalous improbability of my unexplained relationship with some desert nobody must have been bothering him for days.

'Younger than me,' is all I volunteer and he drives on brooding quietly.

'How did I ever get into this?' I ask myself, calculating just how far outside my comfort zone this reunion is going to take me.

'*No visiting Taj Mahal?*' My wish to go straight from Gwalior to one of Agra's marble shops had plainly shocked Opie to the core, but I explained that I'd seen the sights with Mr Sharma. 'Oh, fine, sir.' Shopping was, after all, shopping. I also explained that Sanjay, the Orchha receptionist, had recommended a particular shop. 'No problem, sir. First we go to your place, then to one more shop of this my friend. Very good price, you compare...' However, 'my place' made exactly what I wanted and I placed an immediate order.

Fortunately, Opie took this in his stride, with only the most diffident suggestion that I might consider 'maybe one more table?' Presumably he'll still get a commission from my people. Or maybe he's pinning his hopes on the carpet. Anyway, that's his problem. I have the table that I wanted.

He was, however, right about the Laxmi Vilas Palace: it does seem to be the best in Bharatpur. Unfortunately, he was also right about the pressure on space. The only room available was one without a window, which they keep for emergencies. Well, fair enough: you plan ahead, you get daylight. The important thing is, I'm back in Rajasthan.

There was nothing last night to mark the border, but I knew that I was back where I wanted to be. There were clues in the way people dressed, subtle signs in the way the farmers piled their bullock carts, but mostly just a gut feeling that I was 'home'. Ridiculous, when I've never spent more than three weeks here, but that *is* how I feel: bizarrely, but contentedly, at home. Even if I am tightly wrapped in my heaviest clothes, beside a smoky courtyard brazier.

'I hope you enjoyed your bird-spotting,' says Deepraj Singh, the son of the palace's owner, joining me. 'It was my ancestor who made the sanctuary,' he continues in precise, well-educated English. 'Ironic, because prior to Independence it was his hunting estate. Daily shoots of a hundred thousand birds…'

'This ancestor…' I interrupt him, pulling my own seat closer to the fire. 'Was he the Maharaja?... Before Independence, I mean.'

'He was Maharaja for some years *after* Independence,' he corrects me. 'What the princes lost in 1947 was their power, not their titles. In the British period, they'd been sovereign states, you see… Well, semi-sovereign. They no longer had their private armies, but they'd kept their powers over justice, taxation and so on. Independence did away with all that, leaving just the titles and their "privy purses", which Nehru guaranteed – in perpetuity.' He relishes the word with a grin. 'But Mrs Gandhi, thought differently. In 1971 she stripped them of every last privilege.'

'But they still had their palaces?'

'Yes, but without the income to maintain them. Some took up business careers or went into politics. Others,' he laughs ruefully, looking round him, 'turned to tourism.'

'Good?' asks Opie, as I sift through the photocopied letters and diary entries on the back seat. Deepraj said his father was the historian in the family – if I wanted to know more, I should ask him – and the head of the household has responded as if I were preparing a doctoral thesis, sending me off to visit Deeg, their former capital, with a formidable pile of research materials.

'Fascinating,' I answer tersely, as Opie chuckles, not believing me for a moment. I am, however, finding myself unexpectedly gripped by the detail of these long-gone lives: their family feuds, their dynastic marriages, their aristocratic foibles… until suddenly, without warning, Opie slams his foot on the break and the papers tumble round my feet.

'You want photo?' he asks, oblivious to the disarray. 'Here is camel fair. All are these tourists liking.'

He no doubt envisaged just a simple roadside snap, but I set off down the hillside, into the thick of things. At first, no one pays me much attention and I wander undisturbed amongst the dealers and animals, filming everything in sight. Then some boys get excited. It may be the video, it may be my foreignness, but soon I'm pressed from every side by a dense huddle of laughing, jostling youth. I try to return to the car but, with every step in that direction, the boisterous gathering swells. I'm making no progress and the car remains alarmingly far up the hill. I stumble, as the crush presses closer, filled with a gut-churning fear that I'll soon be trampled in the dust and camel droppings. I struggle back to my feet and look round frantically for a way through the mob. Suddenly a rough, strong hand grabs my arm and I turn in panic, fighting to be free. Then I see that it's Opie.

Our combined efforts forge a way towards the car, only to find it already besieged by another crowd of exuberant youngsters. Opie strains against the rabble to open my door, inching it wide enough for me to scramble in; but now they are wrenching it back again to stop him closing it. I tug as hard as I can, while he pushes furiously from the outside, until at last it clicks closed and I drop the lock. Opie then fights his own way into the front seat. 'All are these uneducated people,' he snorts, as the car pitches violently sideways.

I try not to speculate how I'd have managed without him.

'Which place you stay?' comes the usual question, as we drive into Deeg – except that, on this occasion, Opie's tone suggests genuine anxiety. Perhaps the hotels here are very small indeed. 'First time Mahtani tourist coming,' Opie continues. Well, that's good, I think. It'll take the pressure off the accommodation. Then one of my guidebooks explains the concern. 'Avoid spending a night here,' it counsels bluntly, adding for those undeterred that the government motel has just 'two dirty rooms', while the cheaper Dak Bungalow is 'basic and filthy'. Opie sounds the horn to summon a shoeshine boy and, for a moment, I fear we're seeking the child's advice on the sleeping options; however, he's merely getting directions to what Deepraj called the Pleasure Palaces. 'I know all the places,' he reminds me, reversing a hundred metres up the street.

Old G. H. R. (if Mr Tillotson will forgive the familiarity) wrote eloquently of Deeg's graceful summer pavilions and elaborate formal gardens, but everything today is desolately dry and conspicuously unloved. I feel more in the mood for tigers.

'Are we too late to get to Sariska?' I rouse Opie from his nap.

'Sariska Palace good place,' is his only reply as he starts the engine. I'm increasingly convinced that Opie's notion of a quality hotel is simply one possessed of a drivers' dormitory – almost the norm in the rural palaces and virtually unheard of elsewhere – but, good or bad, the decision is taken. We are on our way to Sariska.

'Later, sir, after Gujarat... In Jaisalmer, sir... Which place you stay? With this young person – your friend – his family?' Surely, so many weeks ahead, he can't already be worrying about his own arrangements. More likely, an unexplained dread of the unconventional in mine. 'All are these tourists liking Heritage Inn,' he adds, as if to confirm the point.

As far as I know, Mohamd still sleeps on the floor in the flat belonging to Riyaz, the shopkeeper friend, and I've no intention of making the carpet more congested. Nor have I much taste for nights in the desert with his parents. As for the Heritage Inn, 'I'll wait and see,' I tell him.

'You have family, sir?' He changes the subject.

'Of course,' I hedge.

'Not liking Rajasthan?' he persists.

'Not really.'

Opie pauses, unsatisfied.

'You have children?' he asks, after a while.

'Actually, no.'

'I have children, sir. One boy, one girl. When you come in this my village you see.'

'Ah, yes…'

'You have wife, sir?' Opie knows better than Mahtani how to get to the heart of things.

'Too expensive,' I tell him, at which he laughs heartily, then turns silent, trying hard to imagine such an undreamed-of state of affairs.

By the time we reach Sariska, I've abandoned any hope of tiger-spotting, but Opie, less easily deterred, strides up to the reception desk, barking 'safari' like a man used to getting his way. A jeep and naturalist are swiftly organised and we are just driving off, when my driver comes running after us. 'Please, sir, how many night you stay?'

'Two?' I answer vaguely. Then I see what he's getting at. 'I suppose I won't really need you tomorrow.'

Opie looks happier than he has all day. 'This my cousin I am visiting. Day after tomorrow come back.'

The nature expert is pointing at his watch: the tigers are getting impatient, it seems. However, just inside the park, we stop at a lake. 'What are those birds?' I ask, without enthusiasm.

'Ducks', he answers.

'I know they're ducks. I was hoping you'd tell me what kind.' He reaches for my bird book. 'Don't worry. I can do that myself. I just thought…' He says he specialises in animals, although it can't be much of a challenge to identify the antelopes and deer, which is all that we see. Not a whiff of a tiger.

It is cold and dark in the jeep, as we return to the hotel. It is cold and underlit in my bedroom. I wish I could leave tomorrow but I've no means of contacting Opie.

I'm trapped.

'Any tiger?' asks Opie, as if he already knows the answer.

We heard some alarm calls yesterday morning, from the peacocks and monkeys; we followed some footprints, with a sense of mounting excitement; then, as the sun began to rise, the calls died down. We saw fresh prints in the evening; we heard further alarm calls, this time from deer; and we were extremely close to the deer, so we must have been close to the tigers, but we never saw a stripe. In a way, I don't mind: I enjoyed the pursuit. What upsets me is the fact that Opie and his cousin went in at midday – the worst possible time – and saw two!

To make matters worse, our proximity to his family prompts a re-run of the dinner-invitation: 'All are these tourists coming to my home. All are very happy. No extra charge I am making...' Then he introduces a complication: 'Wife not well.' Full of guilty relief, I protest that I couldn't, in the circumstances, impose; but he promises she'll be fully fit on the day. I try to remain evasive, yet sense that every failure to give an outright refusal makes my acceptance more complete.

'Car also not well,' he sighs, opening the bonnet and rolling up the sleeves of his first clean shirt since we met. There's a problem with the radiator and, for most of the morning, we keep stopping wherever any form of water is sighted, like camels crossing the desert. In one case, Opie causes outrage at a village pump, elbowing the women aside to fill a bottle. Later, more desperately, he dredges up a muddy litre from a wayside puddle. The new shirt looks like camouflage battledress. So not the best day, you might think, for a substantial detour. 'Samode Palace this way straight,' says Opie, hoping to discourage me; but I have set my heart on the ruined city of Bhangarh.

He saw the warning signs in his mirror. I was poring over a map and Opie is suspicious of maps. He doesn't understand them and resents the secret information that they give me. His knowledge of the roads is impressive but entirely the product of experience. Someone once directed him from A to B; someone else explained the way from B to C; even the track from C to D he used on one occasion. Yet imagine for a moment that A, B, C and D are the four points of a square and he has to get from A to D. He could well drive the long way round, because no one ever showed him the direct route.

'In this Bhangarh… is some tourist activity?' he asks, now resigned to the inevitable. Only one of my books so much as mentions the place, but Opie's ignorance adds greatly to its attraction. The book says it used to boast ten thousand homes, but everything was abandoned when a magician put a curse on it, and today the only sign of life is a group of laughing, chattering boys, combining a swim with their washday chores in a derelict stone water tank. 'Samode many kilometre far,' Opie reminds me, but I insist I need a break and settle to read in the shade of a solitary tree. In no time, the boys have scrambled up the ruins to investigate, peering close enough to drip water on my book, as they shiver in their underpants. The tallest notes the title with a smile. '*In Rajasthan*', he reads aloud to prove his literacy. Then they all lose interest and return to soaping their shirts.

As it happens, the author lives nearby. Her husband used to be a bank manager in Bombay but, like me, he 'stopped' and they now run a farm. The wife had always longed to see the Jaisalmer desert and she writes of a journey over much the same ground as my own intended route, but with a sense of excitement so different from my own of apprehension. However, something in her story suddenly persuades me that I must get the Mohamd business over and done with before Gujarat. I'll call him from Samode.

My room has four large windows facing east, matched by four more the same, facing west. Each has a jali screen, through which the royal women would have peered at a courtyard on one side and the outside world on the other. The latter looks east towards some mountains and, as the sun rises slowly over the crest, the light filters gradually through the first window's tracery, projecting its shafts onto the opposite wall. It starts in finely focussed detail, then softens as it brightens to a climax. The second window follows the same delicate progress and so on down the line, until there are four blazing patterns facing four radiant jalis. It's a lightshow to set my alarm for.

'First time coming to India?' asks the youth who brings my 'bed tea'.

'Second time coming to Samode,' I brag, without admitting that the first was just a daytrip from Jaipur. It was, however, long enough for me to be astounded. I was planning just to soak up the splendour for a couple of nights, then move to the city; but now it occurs to me, there's no need: I can 'commute'. The only snag is the telephones are down – not just to the palace, but to the whole village – and I can't try farther afield, because Opie's taken the car to fix the radiator. Mohamd will have to wait. However, I've given no thought to my day. 'Perhaps a walk in the hills,' I suggest to the receptionist.

'You should go with the bed tea boy,' he advises.

'Isn't there a map?' I protest.

'Better you go with Vijay,' he insists and I set off, full of the usual impotent resentment. Then gradually I notice I'm enjoying his company. He's twenty-seven and married with two young children. Clearly bright, he says he didn't have the right 'background' for university, so he carries bags and brings tea. He has a very straightforward way of knowing and accepting his place.

'We visit Monkey God,' he explains at the top of what he tells me are three hundred and seventy-six steps. There is a temple dedicated to Hanuman just a few kilometres along the ridge and I brace myself for a scramble over rugged, stony ground. Remarkably, however, almost every metre of the way has been neatly paved and a frail old man is working on the last remaining stretch. Many years ago, still a boy, he dreamed that Hanuman had commanded him to devote his life to the project. Now he lives entirely on donations from pilgrims and I happily add my own.

Vijay buys a bag of sweets and, as we enter the temple, rings a bell to let the god know he's there. I'd like to do the same, but fear it might be thought frivolous. A priest places the sweets in a gleaming bucket in front of Hanuman's statue, while Vijay prostrates himself and kisses the floor. Outside, we find a stone coated with bright orange powder. Vijay dips his finger in the powder and, using a mirror provided for the purpose, paints a flawless *tikka* dot in the middle of his forehead. When he does the same for me, I see that I am allowed to join in. I accept Hanuman's blessing and, throughout the day, everyone I meet asks me how I liked the monkey temple. I'm a marked man.

'You are arrrdist?' enquires the crowd in front of the palace gate, where I've set up my painting stool.

'Well, yes… But not a very good artist.'

'No. Verrry gooood arrrdist' goes the refrain. They know nothing of western painting styles, so my faltering efforts are effectively beyond criticism.

One particular small boy appoints himself my protector. He darts round officiously, ensuring that everyone keeps out of my sight lines, fetching water for my brushes, holding my paint box, doing me any possible service. 'Any problem, you tell me, *no* problem. You want, I am getting. You are my brother. You are my friend. You are my best friend.' Eventually, the suggestion is made that, having become his best friend, I might visit his father's shop.

'Have a look in your father's album of business cards,' I tell him. 'You might find my own in there.'

He thinks I'm teasing and wanders off, disappointed in me; but later I find him back at the stall where I once bought a picture. The father recognises me, clasping my hand in both of his, and sure enough my card is still in the album. 'Patrick Moon, Partner,' it reads – now more of a collector's piece than he realises. The boy's faith is restored. 'You come to my house,' he invites me. 'Take tea, chapatis also… Because you are arrrdist.'

I've been admiring the tightly tailored, high-collared jackets worn by the men on reception. 'Nehru jackets,' one of them tells me and I am just on the point of asking whether someone in Samode might be able to make me one when Opie walks in, wearing precisely the garment that I had in mind, and the project loses its appeal. What, I wonder, can have triggered this new sartorial sophistication? Is he suddenly trying harder to look the chauffeur's part? Or has he simply decided that his shirts might last for seven, instead of the usual four days, if he hid them under a jacket?

He was expecting me to be packed up and ready for my move into Jaipur, but quickly adapts to the commuting plan. He's had the radiator fixed and also managed to go home. In fact, his wife has come back with him, because she's still unwell. 'Breathing problem,' he says, thus renewing my hopes of a cancelled dinner date. 'Taking to Jaipur for check-up.'

As I slide into the back seat, I find the front one unexpectedly crowded. Not only is there a woman – Opie's wife, I assume – but also two men, who turn to grin at me. 'My brothers,' says Opie.

'Hospital visiting, after you and me gone. Son and daughter with these my parents,' he adds, in case I was worrying: the extended family in action. I ask whether one of the brothers – or indeed Mrs Opie – wouldn't be more comfortable in the back, but no one will hear of it. Indeed, Opie even takes some persuading to attend to his wife before addressing my plans for the day. 'Hospital only half kilometre far,' he assures me, as he dumps the family party on a busy roundabout. 'Now, sir, first to City Palace?'

'First to telephone,' I tell him firmly, only to discover that Mohamd's number isn't in my diary, as I thought, so I need to ask Andrew and the call is a difficult one – first because Opie's chosen PCO-STD-ISD has been squeezed onto the corner of a crowded refreshment stall; second because he stations himself inquisitively at my elbow; and third because Andrew, busy in his office, doesn't have much sympathy for my Jaisalmer anxieties.

'You've got the number. Just ring him up,' he says briskly. 'If he's forgotten who you are, it'll save you a journey.' I picture him, frowning fiercely behind his lawyerly spectacles, impatient to turn his mind back to more demanding problems. But I can't ring Mohamd now, not with Opie's ears pricking up so intrusively beside me.

'No other friend you like to call?' he prompts, as if he's worked everything out.

'No other friend,' I disappoint him.

'So now to City Palace?' he asks, with a wink at the Tillotson.

'Now to hotel!' A self-defeating show of independence. 'Now to finish painting.'

For the first time, Opie was late. I heard the car long before I saw it: a loud mechanical clanking, reverberating all the way up through the village. 'Shock absorbers,' he informed me, quite impervious to the din. 'Tonight I am fixing.'

'You've been to the hospital?' I shouted, as we rattled off to Amber.

'Yes, sir. Twenty days this my wife they make her stay.' He sounded unusually glum: twenty days would be expensive. 'But home again by Neemrana,' he promised, looking on the bright side; then even more purposeful: 'This morning you take elephant? I know very good man...'

Almost everyone hires an elephant for the steep zigzag climb to the Amber Fort. It's what I did two years ago, but today I'm determined to walk and walking with the elephants proves hazardous: I pay more attention to the one in the video viewfinder than the one about to trample me – not to mention the tendency to trip on turds the size of cannonballs. However, it does have the happy effect of shielding me from the waiting pack of aspirant guides, as anyone not arriving by elephant is invisible.

Still flushed with this independent confidence at the end of the morning, I spot a steep, dusty track leading down from the Fort, in the opposite direction from the elephant compound and the car park. At the bottom I find a simple, unexpectedly rural vegetable market, where a few small-scale farmers have spread out their mouth-watering crops on tattered bits of cloth. I set about filming them, while three wide-eyed, solemn-faced toddlers shadow me shyly from shot to shot. Their delight in the play-back makes my day, but the best is still to come. I now have to find my way back to the other side of the hill – because Opie, parked near the elephants, has no idea where I am. For the first time since I have been in India, *there is nobody who knows where I am*. For a short, exhilarating half hour, I've escaped. I've broken free! And it's my chance to call Jaisalmer.

'Sir, The Mohamd In Village,' says the owner of Cottage Gallery, giving his characteristic stress to every word.

I tell him it's urgent, that I'm hoping to be in Jaisalmer in two days' time. I need to be sure that he'll be there.

Riyaz promises to pass on the message, but I'm far from reassured. How can he hope to make contact with a boy in the desert?

Opie was late again. He'd overslept in the car, having arrived back too late for the drivers' dormitory. On his way to deal with the shock absorbers, the clutch had given out, so he and a mechanic had been up until three, which is why both the driver and the vehicle were so dirty. He bundled up the oil-smeared towelling covers, revealing virgin upholstery underneath. The car remained more than usually redolent of stockinged feet, but I knew I was fortunate not to be wasting the day in a repair yard and a moment later the same thought struck Opie. Only *his* superior engineering skills had saved the day, he insisted, progressing seamlessly to his other inestimable qualities, in case habitual exposure had blunted my appreciation. Then, superlatives exhausted, he turned to the main business of the day: 'Where you stay in this Bikaner?'

I was, however, more than usually deaf to advice. I'd waited a year to return to Bhanwar Niwas. Not for the fine *haveli* architecture. Not even for the cooking. It's the music I wanted to recapture. Some brought tears to the eyes with its melancholy, some sent shivers down the spine with its exuberance, but all of it sung with a full-throated fervour by an elderly man and a ten-year-old boy. Especially the boy. Banish all thoughts of cathedral choristers. This was passionate, primitive, untamed; and I wanted to hear it again.

There's no sign of singers as I deal with my check-in, but the platform where they used to play is still there. I put my things in my room and return to the courtyard, by which time a violinist is tuning his instrument. A tabla player shambles in with his drum, followed surely by the same old man. There's an anxious few minutes while they chat, then at last they start playing. The songs sound familiar. The man's voice is just the same. The unrestrained passion is exactly as I remember it. But no boy.

At reception they tell me: 'Yes, he still sings for us. You have fine memory. And yes, you are right, sir. Boy is good. But tonight he is sick.' I mind this much more than the tigers.

Opie manages not to be late. Instead, he pulls off something more spectacular. It begins when he takes the wrong road. I notice this because all the road-signs point to places which my atlas tells me should be on the other side. I try to convince him but, no, he always takes this route, it's better than the one on my map, he insists, as he surges off down a sandy track; and within half a mile we have sunk into the sand.

He pulls up what he can of the sparse vegetation to push under the wheels. Some workmen wander over and offer to help. The car is jacked up and dug around, but all to no avail, so the workmen lose interest. Opie says he'll walk to the nearest village, leaving me to guard the car. When at last he returns with a camel and a camel driver, they drag us out with impressive ease, yet still it takes an eternity to find our way back to the road, where a sign confirms that our four hour adventure has taken us only twenty miles from Bikaner, leaving six hours to go.

The distant sight of the Jaisalmer Fort should have been an inspiring end to the journey, but it's almost dark by the time we arrive and I'm concerned about finding a room. Opie's Heritage Inn is full and we trail around five or six alternatives, before I settle for a former caravanserai in the old part of town. At least I'll not need the car to go out to dinner.

Not that I want to go out to dinner. I wish I could eat a quick snack and go straight to bed. Then I wouldn't have to face Mohamd, face the fact that he probably won't want to see *me,* this one-time tourist, here to make a nuisance of himself. But I force myself to call the Cottage Gallery.

'Hello, Mohamd? This is your friend, Patrick.' That empty figure of speech, but what else do I call myself?

'Hello, sir.' He sounds friendly enough, but I'll have to do something about the 'sir'.

'I've just arrived. I know it's late, but if it's not a problem, I wondered... I mean, if you haven't already eaten... Will you have dinner with me?'

'If you say so,' he says immediately. 'It's my duty.'

Three

I like the 'duty' even less than the 'sir'. It was meant to be an invitation, not a summons. But we agree that he'll come to the hotel in half an hour.

I change and go down to reception, where there's no sign of him. But why should there be? I'm fifteen minutes early. I'll pace in the garden for a while. No, better to find a seat, try at least to *look* composed. I haven't felt like this since my job interview, twenty years ago. What if he turns out not to be the person I thought I wanted to help? What if we've nothing to say to each other? To take my mind off these and similar questions, I read one of his letters, carried in my wallet:

'How are you, your life and your job? I am quite well here and I hope from God that you will be all right at your place. I am sorry to write you a simple letter on plain paper. You know my condition very well. I am also sorry to write you late. I was little bit lazy. And now I think in your mind you thinking that I (an Indian boy) quite forgotten us completely. Also you thinking that he (I) was a selfish boy like other Indian person which you trusted and they make cheat with you. You can trust me I say you true. You don't think this that I (me) took business from you and he forget us (you). I never forget you in my life. I have seen so many tourist in my life. Lot of tourist tell me we want to help you. But then they going back to their country then all of

*them they quite forgotten me. They never write me in letter
they really want to help me. I can't forget you in my life.…
Write me soon. I am just waiting for your letter. Where you
come in Rajasthan I will come to see you there. I will be
there sure. Write me soon.'*

Suddenly the warmth of his smile is beaming shyly down the
garden path. He looks different, less a boy, more a young man. A
smart pair of moccasins has replaced the scuffed lace-up shoes and
his neatly pressed chinos and long-sleeved shirt would hardly
disgrace Austin Reed. He glances anxiously at a cheap digital watch.

'I was early,' I reassure him and we both laugh nervously. 'I'm
so pleased to see you,' I add awkwardly and try to show as much of
that as a handshake allows.

'This is very good of you, sir…' He looks diffidently away.
'Coming so far to see me.'

'I came to see Jaisalmer,' I tease, finding his face hard to read
and wishing he'd said that he was pleased to see me. 'I was missing
Gadi Sagar.'

'How many days you stay?' he asks keenly. 'Five, six maybe?'

'I've checked in for two nights,' I mumble, feeling ashamed,
asking myself which of us now sounds pleased to see the other. 'I'll
probably stay for three,' I add, without erasing the disappointment
from his face and we both stand awkwardly, Mohamd's eyes
flicking hopefully towards the street.

'Shall we…?' he gestures to the escape route. 'I remember, you
like Trio restaurant, no?'

'My favourite,' I tell him, relieved to have any plan imposed.

'Which way?' It's Mohamd's turn to tease at a shadowy
crossroads. I had forgotten how bewildering Jaisalmer's tangle of
narrow streets is, especially at night, with many of the shops
already closed and dark. I had such vivid memories, I thought it
would all come back to me, that I'd feel at home, able to manage

on my own, if Mohamd turned out to be busy, or if things didn't work out between us. But I quickly see how dependent I am.

As he stops to brush some cow dung off his moccasins, I wonder, not for the first time, how he manages to look so spruce on his budget. As if he has read my mind, he says the shoes are second hand, bought from a tourist for five hundred rupees. Like the watch – in that case, two hundred rupees.

Trio is only a short walk, perhaps ten minutes, but it takes us longer. So many enthusiastic greetings are showered on us by the youth of Jaisalmer. 'Hello, sir. Welcome, sir, Mr Patrick,' says one. 'Mumda speaking always about you,' says another, throwing an arm around Mohamd's shoulder.' I feel both pleased that Mohamd is popular and amused that my own legend has gone before me.

The restaurant is on a rooftop, overlooking a bustling, brightly-lit square. 'What do you recommend?' I ask, eying the gleaming copper dishes on other tables.

'My first time here, sir,' he admits, looking self-consciously round at the other diners, who are mainly tourists. 'But I know the owner,' he adds, as if to restore his credibility. 'One local travel agent. Sometimes giving me guiding work.'

'You choose anyway.' I pass him the menu.

'I think maybe chicken is good,' he suggests.

'Sorry, I meant to say... I'm more or less vegetarian.'

'I think, kitchen very clean,' he tries to persuade me, having no doubt set his heart on an unaccustomed treat. 'Non-veg, I think, would be fine for you, sir.'

'No, you must have chicken and we can share some vegetable dishes.'

'Really, just veg will be fine, sir.'

'Listen, I address him sternly. 'I want you to do two things for me. I want you to have chicken and I want you to stop calling me "sir" – you're my friend, not my guide now.'

'Yes, sir. I mean, friend.' He laughs to cover his confusion.

I apologise for not making contact earlier in the day, explaining the adventures that delayed us in the desert. He shrugs this aside, but I can see how much my arrival mattered, when he tells me how he borrowed a friend's scooter this afternoon, driving all over town to ask for me at every hotel.

'What would you like to drink?' I ask, as a waiter brings mineral water for me and a jug of something riskier from the tap for him.

'Oh…' He clearly hasn't thought beyond the water. 'Maybe Pepsi, please.'

'Are you sure you wouldn't like a beer? I'm having one myself.'

'No, thank you… My father would beat me.'

'You're not serious?' I am startled by this fear of his father. Mohamd must be nineteen now and, on the face of things, living an independent life here in the city. Yet paternal authority clearly reigns supreme, even from a distance. Economically, it's his parents who are dependent on *him*. From what I gathered last time, even the fraction of his modest earnings that he manages to send them makes him the family's major breadwinner. In his shoes, I'd be reminding them which side of that bread is buttered, but it simply wouldn't occur to him.

He pushes a hand through his oil-glossy, sharply cut hair and I notice something else that is different. He no longer sports the red and white earrings of the Nayak community. 'More modern,' is his only explanation. Then he asks after Andrew.

'He's fine,' I assure him and explain about Gujarat.

'How is Mr Andrew's job?' he continues and I hesitate. The question is simple enough – he has asked it in every letter – but then he has always asked about my job as well.

'You know about me?' I ask, wondering what kind of explanation I can give. 'You know that I've stopped being a lawyer?'

'You told me in one letter,' he says inscrutably, leaving me wondering whether he judges the development too momentous for comprehension, or too trivial for comment. So I ask about his own work.

'*Comme ci, comme ça,* you say in French, no?' An impish grin says he knows he's showing off. Quickly serious again, he tells me that his top priority is learning to drive. Then he could offer a composite service, combining the roles of both guide and driver, working outside the confines of Jaisalmer.

'How much of Rajasthan do you know?'

'Only Jodhpur,' he confesses. 'I went there last year by bus. With Gajendra, my friend. He is also guide. We saw one movie, then came back by night...' His excited account trails off. 'Sorry... Do you mind?' He has been struggling with his knife and fork since the food arrived, but is hoping to discard them.

'Of course not. I wish I could manage like you,' I tell him, admiring the effortless rolling of rice and liquid sauces into bite-sized, drip-free balls. 'Anyway... tell me about the driving. Have you started?'

'Gajendra's cousin, he was giving me private lesson – here in Jaisalmer. But the car hit one cow. Seven hundred and fifty rupees to vet I had to pay.' Laughing sheepishly, Mohamd explains how more formal instruction will mean a couple of weeks at a motoring school in Jodhpur, learning basic repair and maintenance skills, as well as the more fundamental art of avoiding cattle. He was supposed to be there now, but he cancelled his tuition when he heard I was coming. He produces a scrap of paper with the school's charges on it: two thousand rupees for the lessons, on top of which he needs to find somewhere to stay. This is a lot for him and I sense that he hasn't actually scraped it all together. Yet I'm sure there's no hint of a hint intended. Prices are simply something that interests him. He assumes that the cost of the course will interest *me* as much as the prices of his moccasins and watch.

Towards the end of the evening, Mohamd asks to be excused and crosses to speak to a severe-looking middle-aged Indian in a Nehru jacket, at the top of the stairs. He gives the man the traditional '*Namaste*' gesture of greeting – palms pressed together in front of him as if in prayer – coupled with a deeper than averagely respectful bow. The man asks him something and Mohamd shakes his head, with a nod towards our table: I am somehow part of the answer.

'Any problem?' I ask, as he resumes his seat.

'This is local travel agent. Like I told you, he owns this place. Sometimes he gives me work, so always I must show respect.'

'He was offering you work for tomorrow, wasn't he?'

'It's not a problem.'

'You'll lose a day's money.'

'He'll find someone else.'

'Your friend, Gajendra?'

'He's already asked him. He usually asks Gajendra first. Gajendra is also Brahmin, like him.'

'You mean, you don't get work unless the Brahmins are busy?'

'And also one Rajput boy. It's not a problem. We're all good friends.' He pauses and frowns. 'Actually, none of us get so much work now. We don't have government permit. Before last year, it was not so bad, but, these days, the police make problem. So mostly work is going to older guides. Many days I just work in Riyaz shop.'

'What do you have to do to get a permit?'

'We have to pass one exam,' he says glumly. 'And the last chance to sit exam was eight years before.'

'That's all the more reason why you shouldn't lose a day's money. I'm sure I could manage on my own.'

'Oh, come on!' he chides me, laying a reproving hand on my forearm. 'You've come so far. It's my duty. Tomorrow we go to Gadi Sagar, no? You said you were missing.'

'Oh, that was a sort of joke. But yes… Whatever you think.'

'How was food?' he enquires, as we get up to leave.

'Just as I remembered it,' I tell him, but the truth is, tonight I hardly noticed.

'Have you met my driver?' I asked Mohamd, as we queued in reception to confirm my third night. 'He's a bit of a character.'

'I saw one Delhi driver outside. We didn't speak.'

'So he didn't tell you how much better than you he knows Jaisalmer?' I laughed.

Opie, waiting beside the Ambassador, ignores Mohamd's greeting but cheerfully returns mine. Meanwhile, Mohamd has opened the car door to usher me into the back seat – something Opie hasn't done since our first day in Khajuraho and he promptly shows his displeasure by throwing himself into the driver's seat and revving the engine. Mohamd, however, has also opened the front nearside door, intending to assume for himself the usual guide's position beside the driver, on the other side of the subtle but impregnable barrier that defines every occupant's status. This innocent allocation of the seating is about to fix our relationship as one of rigid inequality, negating most of my purpose in coming here; yet stupidly, unimaginatively, I've failed to anticipate it.

'Do you want to sit there or in the back?' is my only limp response.

'As you wish, sir.'

'Hey, no sirs!'

'Sorry... Patrick.'

'I think in the back,' I continue just as feebly and, as he inches hesitantly into the unfamiliar territory beside me, I have a powerful sense of Opie's eyebrows straining not to raise themselves at this outrageous levelling of the natural order. But I had to get this right. I came here to find out how I could help this boy and I can't do that if I keep him at a distance.

On the way to Gadi Sagar, Opie talks exclusively to Mohamd, asking a barrage of questions in rapid, surly-sounding Hindi. Mohamd's answers are short, mainly monosyllabic. In one case, I hear him say 'Nayak'; in most of the others, something negative. Sitting directly behind Opie, I'm unable to read his reaction. However, when we reach the lake, he instantly leaps from behind the wheel to wrench my door open, standing so stiffly to attention that I almost expect him to salute. I am Opie's client, let everyone remember, not this young upstart's.

'Is it how you remember?' asks Mohamd, apparently oblivious to all this.

'Less water,' I mumble, preoccupied with Opie. 'But just as beautiful.'

'It was a bad monsoon,' he explains, as we reach a waterside temple. 'Is OK I tell you again about these places?'

'Of course,' I answer but, as soon as the standard patter is exhausted, I suggest a quiet walk round the lake.

'Normally tourists don't have time,' he says, then pauses thoughtfully, before continuing in a different vein. 'First time you came, I never tell you …' He hesitates, then it all comes out in a rush of nostalgic pride. 'Gadi Sagar is the place I first make small business, selling fossils, eleven years old. You see there in distance, some buildings? That is one hostel. I was living there, going to school in city. Early morning, many tourists visiting lake. I come here before schooltime, hide my school bag, sell fossils, then change behind temple into uniform, get to school by ten-thirty. Evening time, I make better business, not here, but Sunset Point – last time you did not see – tourists coming there five, six o'clock for sundown and school finish four-thirty, so again I hide uniform, take fossils. Many tourists there, more than Gadi Sagar, but also more police. After, I go back to hostel. Three boys I share room with, they keep my food hot.'

'Did you make much money?' I ask, when he pauses for breath.

'Enough for hostel and for school things. Later, I promoted myself – selling camera films, making little bit more. Sometimes I make enough to help my parents, in village.'

'When did you "promote" yourself to guiding work?'

'There was one man, one guide, like me from poor family. Called Manu, but I call him Guru,' he laughs. 'Sometimes, when I'm small boy, he look after me. Maybe I have problem with hostel or police and he help. Also he teach me. You know, Manu, he don't even read or write, but he know everything about Jaisalmer, all learned from other guides. So one day I say to him, "Please, you let me come with you. Tell tourists I carry shopping. Then I listen." '

'And that's how you learned all you know? From this Manu? While you carried the shopping?'

'It's how I started.' He smiles modestly. 'I learn new things every day. I need to study more, but I am little bit lazy.'

We have completed our circuit of the lake and have been sitting on a low stone wall, against which Mohamd is kicking one of his heels. The second-hand moccasins, he explains, are really too small for him, so he's trying to ease the pressure on his toes: the price of high fashion on a low budget. He shows me a neat, triangular patch covering a hole in one of the shoes. Then, more proudly, he shows me the matching fake patch on the other, looking for all the world like some designer gimmick of the manufacturer. And all for twenty rupees, he adds with satisfaction.

'Can we come back another day?' I ask, admiring his ingenuity. I've been struck by the finely carved yellow sandstone of the temples and I'd like to paint a picture.

'You mean tomorrow?' he asks. 'You stay just three nights, no?'

'I may stay longer… I don't want to stop you working but I thought, maybe a day in the desert? The proper desert,' I emphasise.

'Not that tiny patch of sand, where Mahtani's camels took us.'

'We can go to there now,' he offers gamely.

'Better tomorrow,' I suggest, noting how fast time has flown: it's already midday.

'You feeling maybe little bit tired?' The last time he asked this, I ended up shopping *chez* Riyaz.

'Also hungry,' I emphasise, thinking that, in any case, we both need a rest from the process of finding our way with each other. 'I think my hotel does snacks…'

'We could go to Cottage Gallery, take lunchbreak there,' he presses. 'Always Riyaz he is asking, how is Mr Patrick…' And so I find myself back on the velvet-upholstered customer bench, with a newspaper parcel of take-away samosas, fetched in by Riyaz's brother. As before, Mohamd disappears to chat with friends in the street, while I look longingly at the chink of daylight round the edge of the door, wishing I could be with him after all, instead of being polite about the avalanche of craftwork descending from the shelves.

'I Tell You Honestly, Sir. This Best Quality. You Try Other Shop In Jaisalmer, You Not Find Like This…' I feel I have skipped a whole year back in time.

Riyaz looks plumper than I remember, more pampered by success perhaps, yet still with the same avuncular warmth that has made him – only four or five years the senior of the two – Mohamd's protector. The shop is now more specialised, with one wall devoted entirely to neatly folded Kashmir shawls, ranging from sheep's wool to luxurious pashmina. There are also some Kashmiri durry carpets – over three times the price of my Jodhpur man, but finer.

'All very nice,' I mumble. 'But I'm not really shopping.'

'Definitely, Sir. No Need To Buy. Just You See The Quality. This Hundred Per Cent Hand Made…' He drapes a shawl round my shoulders.

'Well, I'm here for a couple of days...' I get up too quickly, kicking over my glass of tea.

'Most Welcome, Sir. Any Time. This Colour Very Perfect.' He advances with a second shawl.

'No, honestly, I bought one last time.'

'For Your Friend, Mr Andrew?'

'I'll think about a carpet,' I promise stupidly.

'Please, Sir, No Need To Buy.' He laughs at the absurdity of the idea. 'I Show You Because I Know You Love The Art. But, Sir, Please...' He smiles as a new inspiration dawns. 'While You Stay Here In Jaisalmer, I Hope You Do Me Great Honour. You Come Take The Dinner In My Home.'

'That's very kind, but I haven't even thanked you for lunch yet.'

'It Is My Pleasure, Sir. Because All What You Do For The Mumda. Please, Sir, Five-Thirty Today You Come.'

'Could we make it later?' I ask, hoping for just a little time to myself. 'Perhaps seven-thirty?'

'Definitely, Sir. As You Like.'

Suddenly the door opens, filling the shop with sunlight, as Mohamd stands silhouetted in the opening like a rescuing angel. 'Shall we...?' he motions towards the street.

He stresses that he's instructed Riyaz not to pay him commission on anything I buy. He wants me to get the best price, but I tell him I have so far stood firm. 'As you like,' he assures me, with an enigmatic grin born of many hours watching Riyaz in sales mode; then, as if suddenly anxious how best to amuse me: 'Is OK now we go to City Palace?'

I hesitate. A return there ought to form part of my Rajput architectural studies, but I had enough tourist spiel at the lake. Now, with Mohamd at my side, there's a chance to understand some more ordinary things in the bazaar: what the street-side cobbler and his pompous-looking customer are arguing about, what the runny-nosed little boy with no underpants thinks is funny… Mohamd also helps me find the smallest CD shop in the world, occupying no more than a passage between two tailor's shops, the counter just a narrow shelf, with barely space for the customer on one side and the thinnest salesman they could hope for on the other.

I started a small collection of Indian classical music at a service station on the way to Jaisalmer and the stock here proves large enough for me to double it. Spotting a tape of Indian pop songs, Mohamd asks me to lend him the necessary rupees until tonight. He has no machine to play it on but says he can listen at a friend's house. With difficulty, I persuade him to accept it as a belated birthday gift. Then a thought strikes him: 'I think, this afternoon you are not needing car, no? Tonight also, we can walk to Riyaz home…'

'Of course,' I interrupt, wondering what he has in mind.

'Maybe we should tell the driver.' I clap my forehead in shame. I had completely forgotten about Opie. He must still be parked round the corner from the shop. We ought to go back there. 'No need to worry.' Mohamd beckons to a diminutive youth who was waving to us from the steps of an imposing haveli. 'This is Ravi, you remember? My old school friend.' Ravi's eager, outstretched hand indicates that he remembers me, but his beaming, childlike features ring no bells. 'Last time we sat on rooftop, over his father's shop,' Mohamd prompts. 'Watching girls,' he adds shyly, as the friend's face cracks into a lecherous grin, exposing teeth stained red from chewing betel nuts. 'Ravi can run and tell the driver…'

I start to protest but Ravi puts up a hand to curtail me. 'It's my duty,' he insists inexplicably.

'I think you are feeling boring,' Mohamd frets, as we continue on our way.

'But I love it here,' I tell him, sounding less than convincing. I wish I could make him understand how this gentle exploration of the simple sights of the bazaar has unexpectedly made India seem closer, its skin less impenetrable. It's as if I've been looking at the country through net curtains and Mohamd has at last drawn them back, making everything miraculously brighter and sharper. I could almost hug him with the excitement of it.

As the afternoon advances, he grows increasingly concerned about the possible presence of police, on the look-out for unlicensed guides. We walk a few yards apart, like an adulterous couple, pretending not to know each other in the presence of suspicious spouses, until at last our illicit assignation can resume on Ravi's rooftop where, as before, there is a girl – surely the same girl – on a distant roof terrace.

'I was waiting for the right moment,' I tell him, taking a small parcel from my shoulder bag. 'This is your real birthday present.'

He unwraps the neatly compact binoculars that I picked up in Duty Free, hoping he'd like them. Instinctively he trains them on the girl. He was in love with her, he says. For about six months. He used to go past her house every day on his way to school. She would smile and talk to him from her window. They never 'went out together' but if a day passed without seeing her he couldn't sleep. Then he made himself stop. She came from a different caste. 'Sorry.' He turns a moist pair of eyes back to me. 'I didn't say thank you.'

'It's nothing,' I squeeze his shoulder, as he bites his lip.

His parents intend for him the most traditional of arranged marriages. Not only will he get no say in the selection of his bride, he won't even meet her – or know anything about her – until the ceremony. She will naturally come from the Nayak community, but there are not so many Nayaks in the region and those that there are live in desert villages, where sons receive little enough education and daughters none at all. It is clear from the clenching of his knuckles how much this troubles him. I think he could just about come to terms with the lack of personal choice, if he thought there was the slightest chance of a meeting of minds. As it is, he sees a life sentence of incompatibility hurtling inexorably towards him.

'But you could always say "no"?'

He shakes his head, laughing gently at my naivety. 'It would ruin my family,' he says simply.

'But it's *your* life. Surely, if you explained things…'

'You don't understand,' he continues grimly. 'If I said "no", my parents would lose their place in society. No one would have anything to do with us. No one would even let their daughters marry my brothers.'

'Please be comfortable.' Mohamd points to the rug on the concrete floor of the one room apartment, while Riyaz takes a solitary cushion from behind a curtain and urges me to prop it behind my back. The curtain must be hiding their clothes, their rolled up bed mats and whatever little else they own between them, for the room is otherwise starkly empty.

'Sir, You Mind First We Have Dinner, Later Talk?' asks Riyaz, as his brother hurries in with food from their tiny kitchen. It's Ramadan and Riyaz, I should have realised, is Muslim. He must last have eaten before dawn and you can tell at a glance that abstinence doesn't come easily. As he passes me the mutton – clearly their special treat for me – he is visibly desperate for his own helping.

Using the knife and fork that they borrowed from a neighbour, I accept a little of the mutton but take mainly the vegetarian dish. Riyaz frets that I'm not eating enough, that I can't be liking the food, while Mohamd whispers an apology that there's no beer. I'm entirely happy with the vegetables and the specially purchased mineral water, but the more I protest the less they believe me.

'Sir, You Like Tea Now?' asks Riyaz as soon as I finish. 'Or Maybe In Shop?' He is plainly concerned not to miss any passing evening trade, so I opt for the shop where, as usual, Mohamd slips outside to the street, while Riyaz lays out the carpet that I liked. 'Sir, You Not Find Like This In Jodhpur. This Best Quality...'

I remind him that the Jodhpur man is much cheaper.

'I Tell You Honestly, Sir, This Price Very Special Price. This No Profit Price...'

I repeat that I simply cannot afford it. Then another tactic occurs to him and he takes out some finely detailed miniatures painted on antique paper. Seeing me linger for a moment over a particular pair, he offers to throw in one of these with the carpet. I tell him, I'm sure it's a bargain, but I no longer earn that sort of money.

'Sir, This Price You Never See In Jaisalmer. This Price Only For Mumda's Special Friend...'

I tell him I certainly can't afford both the carpet and a picture, but then, more to fill a silence than anything else, find myself asking, what would be his absolute best price for the carpet on its own? I never intended to get into this conversation. There was never any point in trying to bargain. After all, what could he possibly come down to that would be less than extravagant for me?

Riyaz names a figure almost twenty per cent lower than the zero-profit, lowest possible one previously quoted, telling me that the discount is a present, to thank me for my kindness to Mohamd. He says it in a way that makes it seem ungrateful to refuse. At this level, he assures me, he will be making a loss. He goes almost so far as to say that he'll be ruined but, as I sign the credit card slip, I remind myself 'There's no such thing as a free mutton curry.'

Opie seems more talkative. With Mohamd, that is. He is seldom less than talkative with me; but this morning, as we drive into the desert, the non-stop Hindi monologue means that even Mohamd scarcely gets a word in, merely what I take to be a 'yes' or a 'no' or a 'well I never', every other minute. From the look on his face, I imagine he is hearing the original language version of Opie's many and varied virtues, more familiar to me in translation. Certainly his surreptitious wink seems to say, 'You were right. A bit of a character!'

Normally, I wouldn't mind – it gives me a welcome break from Opiespeak – but today it stops me telling Mohamd my news. Or maybe that's the point: Opie's cunning plan to drive a wedge down the middle of the back seat, reasserting his proprietorial rights.

'You see, sir.' Opie finally addresses me, as he parks near the gateway to the ruined village of Kuldhara, which Mohamd wants to show me. 'I know all the places. Not like other Delhi drivers, all going only Fort, City Palace, Gadi Sagar...' His paean of self-congratulation tails off, as Mohamd darts nimbly round the back of the car to open my door for me, reminding him too late of the new regime. 'I am waiting here,' he mutters, annoyed with himself.

'I've met your guru,' I tell Mohamd, as soon as we're on our own. 'First thing this morning. You see, the hotel's full tomorrow night, except for an expensive suite. So, when I woke up early, I thought I'd try to find my way up to the Fort. There was a little place I spotted yesterday, when we were walking round. Only five rooms. But it's got this amazing roof terrace, part of the battlements of the Fort...'

'Killa Bhawan?' Mohamd laughs, delighted. 'You met Manu?'

'Yes. I really liked him. And he's very proud of you. Like a father almost. He told me about those times when you were small. But he's full. I'll have to take the suite after all.'

'Just one more night?' asks Mohamd resignedly.

'It's a long way down to Gujarat.'

'Of course.' He falls silent for a while, then remembers that he hasn't told me anything about the Kuldhara ruins. It was really a small town, he explains. Seven hundred homes, built by so-called Paliwal Brahmins – members of the priestly caste but, in this case, a highly successful sub-caste of bankers and traders. Then suddenly, in the eighteenth century, it was abandoned in a single night.

'What made them leave?' I ask, noting how his knowledge seems to have deepened in a year.

'There was one Minister called Salim Singh. You remember I told you? The one who built that big *haveli* in the Fort. Well, he was very much hated and the problem was he had spotted one pretty girl here that he wanted to marry. That's why they all had to leave.'

'Wasn't it a bit drastic? I mean, hundreds of families abandoning their homes, just to save one young girl from a disagreeable husband?'

'That wasn't the point. He wasn't a Brahmin, you see.'

'Oh, of course. A Rajput, I suppose – being a Singh.'

'Not even that. A merchant. A Vaisya.'

'But you said they were traders themselves.

'Brahmin traders. It's different.'

'So I'm beginning to see.'

'It wasn't just this village. There were eighty-three others. All abandoned in the same night. And no one knows where they went. Just vanishing. According to peoples.'

'Incredible… You'd better be careful with those binoculars,' I tease him. 'We don't want the whole of Jaisalmer evacuated.'

Mohamd laughs shyly. 'She waved to me this morning,' he confesses, looking down at his feet.

'I thought you'd decided not to see her?'

'Sometimes I still walk that way,' he mumbles. 'But tomorrow…' he reverts to more practical matters. 'For desert safari, I am thinking, I ask my father for our family camels, unless already some travel agent is booking them. Then the camelman, he cook for us lunch in the desert. We start from city, so you can make free day for Opie.'

'Sounds perfect,' I tell him, meaning the last bit especially.

We climb some dilapidated stairs to one of the few surviving rooftops. 'Please be comfortable,' Mohamd suggests, brushing dust from a rough stone parapet. 'How about sun?' he fusses, as I sit. 'Is it too much of heat?'

'I'm fine,' I insist. 'I just need to change my video film.'

Unpersuaded, Mohamd sits beside me, watching me remove the old cassette. Then, like some dutiful surgeon's assistant, he helps me peel away the cellophane from a new one. It's an oddly intimate moment, made all the more so when he passes me a tiny, postage-stamp-sized photograph from his wallet. I thought it was going to be the girl but instead it shows a pretty, fair-skinned, almost European-looking boy, with an unforgettable smile, winking cheekily beneath a mop of curly black hair. 'We call him Pepsi,' says Mohamd affectionately.

'Why Pepsi?' I laugh.

'It's what he likes to drink. He's only twelve, I think, or thirteen. He's like I was at that age.' He pauses thoughtfully, weighing his words. 'I really love this boy,' he says finally. 'More than all my family. Sometimes, if tourists don't mind, I take him with me, let him carry their shopping.'

'Are you *his* guru?' I ask and Mohamd chuckles modestly.

'One day, I hope, my own son is like him.' As he takes the photograph back again, I ponder the fact that, if I'd had a son, he'd be more or less Mohamd's age. I'd have known him at Pepsi's age… at all his ages.

We've walked well beyond the village, scrambling down a stony bank into what appears to be a dried up riverbed. 'The bad monsoon?' I ask, as Mohamd crouches, peering closely at the pebbles underfoot.

'River only in rainy season,' he explains, searching for something in the dust. 'There, look!' He holds up a small, shell-like object for my inspection. 'It's a fossil – like I used to sell. This is where I came for them.' I join him in the search and, with a lump in my throat, picture a boy like the boy in the photograph doing what we are doing now. Mohamd quickly finds five or six, while I find none; then he stops. 'I think definitely you are feeling boring. Just near, some small Jain temples we can see.'

I wish I could explain how much I'd rather linger here, scrabbling in the riverbed, looking for memories. Instead, I zip a small selection of fossils inside a jacket pocket and return to the car to find Opie pacing restlessly. 'All are these tourists having the right idea in giving this a miss,' he appears to be thinking.

Before we've driven far, Mohamd starts giving Opie directions, apparently to leave the main track. Opie gestures ahead, protesting, I sense, that he doesn't need help, that he does, as he may have mentioned, 'know all the places'. Mohamd, however, presses his point and, scowling, Opie does as he is bidden, motoring truculently on, until Mohamd gives the signal to stop.

Opie looks incredulous. The buildings before us can hardly be the temples. There are two single-storey huts, barely visible behind a perimeter wall – one of them flat-roofed, the other topped with a sagging, ragged-edged thatch. In common with the outer wall, they are crudely built from mud and rubble, yet someone has taken the trouble to paint them in a deep yellow ochre, decorated with simple, stylised patterns, picked out in white and raw siena.

'This is first time I bring tourist,' says Mohamd, as he beckons me across the stony ground. 'But you come not as tourist. You come as my friend.'

Four

I had no illusions that the family farm would be other than modest, no expectations of gleaming combine harvesters or herds of plump cattle; yet still I was unprepared for something so small or so primitive. Nothing grows out here at this time of year and the solitary goat scratching its nose in the dust near the wall does so without any evident optimism.

There are three young children in the gateway. Two are barefoot; one wears plimsolls and a pair of knee-length red stockings, each with a hole in it as big as his knee. Otherwise, an assortment of ill-fitting, ill-matching garments has been shared, apparently at random, between them. They all look delighted to see Mohamd but timid in the presence of a car and its unfamiliar occupants. 'My sister's children,' he says, as they wrap their arms round his chinos. They are all, I notice – even the tiniest, barely able to walk – wearing the same red and white earrings that he used to. 'My sister's living here,' he explains. 'Husband in nearby village has drinking problem, so daytime my mother looks after children, while my sister works, breaking stone in one quarry. Other two sisters, also next village, same. You see, my parents, three daughters, then three sons. One brother older, one younger…'

'Your sisters break stone?' I interrupt, incredulous.

'Also husbands – when they don't drink. It's only work there is here, except in rainy season when there's millet to sow and harvest.'

'And your brothers? Do they break stone?'

He shakes his head, as the children drag him towards the gateway. 'My younger brother's only fourteen, and the older… well, he's the oldest son…'

'Does that exempt him from stone-breaking?'

Mohamd laughs. 'He just finished training to be a primary school teacher.' Then one of the children whispers something in his ear. 'She says both my brothers are gone to city,' he translates, as we duck through the gateway to a small courtyard. 'Also my father. Only my mother is here.'

There is, however, no immediate sign of the maternal presence. Mohamd makes for the nearest of the buildings, the one with the flat roof, but there's no one inside. It is smaller than my present, not over-large hotel room, but he tells me it's the main indoor living and sleeping space for everyone. Yet there is only one rickety *charpai* bed and no prizes for guessing who sleeps there.

'Where do you sleep?' I ask. 'When you're at home.'

'On the roof in summertime,' he says. Squeezed in with everyone else for the rest of the year, I assume. The other building, he explains, is the kitchen and from it, as if on cue, an elderly, dark-skinned, rake-thin woman emerges, bearing three steaming glasses on a small tin tray. The children must have given her a tip-off. 'My mother's made us tea,' says Mohamd.

I'm astonished – not by the tea, although it does smell peculiar; rather by the fact that this stooping, wrinkled figure is Mohamd's mother. I'd assumed her to be an older neighbour, even a grandmother, but she must be my own near-contemporary. Clearly, just as life here makes the young grow up faster than in Europe, so the grown-ups much more quickly grow old. As if reading my thoughts, Mohamd tells me that his parents are past working, that his younger brother is expected soon to take over the farm, such as it is. 'My father's forty-seven,' he says to reinforce the point, making me wonder just how youthful he imagines me to be.

'The tea's made with goat's milk,' he explains. 'Is it OK for you? We make it same like cow's milk *chai* – tea, milk and sugar boiled up together. Not like English tea I drink one time with tourist.'

That explains the smell, I think to myself. 'Will you say, it's very kind of her?' Mrs Nayak merely nods at Mohamd's paraphrase, her face half-concealed behind the veil of her sari, as I psych myself up for a taste. 'Is the third one for Opie?' I ask, in the hope of creating a distraction.

'I'll take it,' he answers, leaving me stranded with his mother, who has now decided that her face should be fully hidden in front of a stranger. I fear my staring may have upset her and I wish I knew how to apologise. However, I was unprepared for the Nayak tribal jewellery. The pendants stretching down from each earlobe would look intimidating on their own, without the elaborate, silver chain linking one of these to a nose ring. Meanwhile, dozens of densely packed white bangles cover every inch of flesh from elbow to armpit. Mohamd's transition from this world is breath-taking.

He returns with Opie's *chai* untouched. He says he doesn't drink it. A wise policy, I decide, after a sip, but I make myself drain the glass, only to see my hostess advancing with a refill.

'Shall we…?' Mohamd comes to my rescue, leading me out of the courtyard, and we walk in silence past the car, past other similar homes, towards the edge of the village. His silences are starting to feel comfortable, companionable; but this one seems different.

'Is anything the matter?' I ask him.

He shakes his head; then, as if angry with himself: 'Just, I'm sorry I've nowhere to give you better welcome.' I tell him not to be foolish but he starts to explain how, in 1947, his father crossed the border from what is now Pakistan at the age of six. It was the time of Partition – the division of territory between Hindu India and Muslim Pakistan. Like so many millions making that journey, his family left behind almost everything they had to start a new life on this little patch of desert. As a child, his father often went hungry. It was many years before they managed even the modest living standards that Mohamd has known. 'They tried hard for us,' he says, looking back at the family home. 'Now, if I make good money, it's my turn to look after them. Also brothers and sisters, when I can.'

'What about your older brother. Doesn't he contribute?'

'He doesn't have a job. He didn't like the school where the government wanted to send him. Too far from the village.'

I don't find myself warming to this brother.

'You said your family were Hindus?' I ask, as we cross some stony scrubland towards nothing in particular.

'Of course,' he answers, as if to say: why else would they leave Pakistan? 'Also we believe in local gods, family gods, but yes we are Hindu.'

'Why did they give you a Muslim name?' I ask, thinking this can only remind them of all that they were forced to abandon. Was it a gesture of defiance? Even one of forgiveness?

'They just liked it,' he laughs, but somehow I can't believe it's that simple. 'I think again you are feeling boring,' he worries.

I fumble for the words to say how privileged I feel to be here, but can see that he doesn't understand. Still anxious how to entertain me, he stoops for a couple of stones, one brick red, the other mustard yellow, explaining how they grind these up to make paints for the village houses. More moved than I dare let him see, I zip them safely away with the fossils.

'You're sure you want to stay?' I ask at Gadi Sagar. 'I'm a very slow painter.'

'Time is not so important,' Mohamd answers, but he is plainly nervous about joining me at the water's edge. He fears a police patrol, yet he's reluctant to wait with Opie, so he settles on some nearby steps. 'I've applied for a passport,' he calls, as I set up my painting stool. 'Riyaz say it take months. Visa even longer...' I remember now: I told him in a letter, I'd buy him an air ticket to London, but I never really thought much about the practicalities. I suppose I never believed he'd be up to the challenge. Or considered whether I would be. 'I think maybe summertime is best,' he continues excitedly. 'England not so cold. Also low season here. Six or eight weeks, you said, no?...' I must have been out of my mind. Even my oldest and closest friends come for three nights max. 'Riyaz can help with visa form,' Mohamd chatters on. 'Two years before, one tourist invite him to Grimsby. He like very much.'

'And afterwards?' I ask. 'Did he find it hard coming back?'

'He found it difficult. But no regrets. I think also I would be fine, no?'

'Be careful,' I remember Elektra warning. 'You'll give him this brief glimpse of our world, then he'll have to go back. It might break his heart.'

'What would you do with him?' asked Alex. 'He can't spend two months watching the Changing of the Guard.

'He might try to stay,' cautioned Andrew.

'I shouldn't worry,' laughed another friend, an immigration lawyer. 'He'll be lucky to get the visa in the first place.'

'You remember yesterday,' Mohamd continues more urgently, 'I tell you my parents want I marry village girl? Many boys here, they have same problem, but only three I know have... how you say?... broke out. One to US, one to France, one to UK...'

'You mean they stayed abroad?' I interrupt, remembering Andrew's admonition.

'No,' Mohamd laughs, as if guessing my concern. 'All came back. But first they make some success.' He explains how, for these young men, the prestige of their Western accomplishments was sufficient to outweigh the stigma of a love match, allowing them to escape the shackles of tradition. He believes that, if he could do the same, even his own parents might set him free. Personally, I can't see what he could hope to achieve in Europe, but then I could never have imagined what he has accomplished *here*. I mustn't underestimate what might be possible, with sufficient cheek and humility.

Mohamd spends most of the long afternoon watching patiently from the steps. Occasionally he disappears to buy us Pepsis, but mostly he discreetly polices the children who approach to compare the lake with its painted likeness. Those who speak a few words of English offer the usual uncritical praise, but the meticulous treatment of the waterside architecture sits uneasily beside my freer handling of the reflections. They belong to different paintings and I have all but decided to give up, when a handsome youth swaggers over to look. He is tall, broad-shouldered and hugely self-confident. Mohamd introduces him and he shakes my hand, oozing charismatic charm. He asks me how I like India, how I like Jaisalmer, how I like Gadi Sagar. He is tactful enough not to ask how I intend to become a better painter.

'This boy is one of these I spoke about,' says Mohamd, when he has gone. 'The one who went to US.' He laughs self-consciously. 'He is playboy. One rich American lady take him back to her home…'

It seems that international success takes many forms. 'Surely that's the answer for you,' I tease him.

'I don't have much experience as playboy.'

Grinning ruefully, he asks if I'll excuse him, then soon returns with a friend's motorscooter, intent on taking me back to the hotel. Opie has, of course, been waiting all afternoon, with a view to doing the same, but Mohamd brushes this aside: all that Opie need do is deliver my equipment to reception. I assume that some detour must be planned, some sight that he wanted to show me on the way; but no, we go straight to the hotel to find Opie unloading the painting stool from the boot.

'Day after tomorrow leaving?' he confirms tight-lipped, handing Mohamd the stool.

'What are you thinking?' asks Mohamd. We have been sitting in silence in the Natraj rooftop restaurant, watching the parade of passing humanity down below, but I am grateful for a cue to voice my feelings.

'How sad I'll be to leave Jaisalmer,' I tell him and he smiles, assuming this to be merely politeness.

'I am also sad,' he says. 'We have only one day more. Usually, with tourists I am feeling boring, but today it was different.' He laughs, determined to resist any mawkishness. Like a conjuror, he whips out a flashy pair of sunglasses, pulling a zany grin as he puts them on to make me laugh as well. 'One tourist gave to me,' he says, then turns serious again. 'Did I tell you about Japanese lady?' I shake my head. 'One time when I was maybe four years old, some Japanese tourists, they came to our village. I don't know why. Normally nobody comes there. But this lady, very rich lady, she wanted to take me away with her to Tokyo. She wanted a son. She asked my parents and they said, yes, if I wanted to go, she could take me, she could give me a better life. But when they asked me, I said "no". I ran away, inside the house. I didn't want to leave all my family, my village, the only world I knew. Now I wish I'd said "yes".' We sit silently again. Then Mohamd finds the words that I should have found: 'But that way we'd never have met.'

'Can you come back next month for Desert Festival?' he asks, suddenly bright and purposeful.

'I wish I could,' I assure him. 'But I have to meet Andrew.'

'Then maybe *I* come to *Gujarat*... see Mr Andrew... but after Festival. In those days, even guides with no permit get work. You know Gujarat dates?'

'I'll bring my diary tomorrow.' I sound less eager than he deserves, but I feel worried about the practicalities, not least his status in relation to Mahtani's guide. Then I recall the geography. Gujarat must be five times as far as he has ever travelled and, he says it himself, he's lazy. He won't come.

The raucous clamour of a wedding band breaks in on these thoughts. It is very much the 'marriage season' – something to do with the stars apparently, prompting ceremonies at all hours of day and night to match the timings decreed by the astrologers. Everywhere you look the homes of brides and grooms are decked with fairy lights, flashing for days; the streets congested with slow-moving processions, often hundreds of well-wishers, escorting grooms to brides' houses or happy couples back to the grooms' homes the next day, each stopping every few minutes, either for refreshments at the house of some senior family member or, wherever the road is wide enough, for bouts of hyperactive dancing to blaring music. No wonder the subject is preying on Mohamd's mind.

'I still have time,' he says. 'Two or three years, I think. My older brother must marry before me and he's not even engaged. First he need job.' Well, that should give you a lifetime, I think privately, but Mohamd continues with untypical urgency: 'Do you think for England, this summer is possible?'

'Andrew could bring the forms,' I tell him. 'We've a lawyer friend, who knows about these things. But you mustn't come hoping to make your fortune – or even to find work. The important thing is to see what you're up against, explore what might be possible. If nothing else, the experience should make you better able to understand the West, leave you better equipped to deal with European tourists... Then, at the end of your stay, you'll have to come back to India to think it all through. But just don't expect any of it to be easy. England is very different from everything you know. You have to be prepared to be disappointed, even to fail.'

It's not that he is short of ideas. He's bursting with them. They are simply not in tune with the realities of English life. His instinctive thoughts are of street-corner salesmanship, with a suitcase full of Kashmiri shawls, but I gently sketch in the cultural differences between Bond Street and the Jaisalmer bazaar. He bounces swiftly back, proposing language lessons for would-be Hindi speakers. I hint that it may be a while before Western demand for his own tongue matches India's interest in English. Undaunted, he imagines himself as a driver for some wealthy Londoner and my mind fills with lurid images of Indian motoring conventions transplanted to Mayfair.

Pausing for breath, Mohamd passes some *papad* – poppadoms topped with chilli and onion – devouring two in quick succession. 'If I don't eat chilli maybe two, three times a day, I feel bad,' he confides, between mouthfuls, and I'm filled with new misgivings. *What will he eat in England?* We can't cook curry three times a day for six weeks! *Where will he sleep?* I know he's used to the floor, but surely we'll have to get a bed... And most delicate of all, but it has to be faced: *how do I teach him about toilet paper?!?*

'You'll have to make *papad* for us,' I tell him, wishing I'd never started this.

'I can't cook *anything*,' Mohamd confesses, unaware of my anxieties.

'I'll still buy you a ticket,' I laugh, but he insists he'll pay me back when he makes enough money. Then he excuses himself. The restaurant belongs to Gajendra's uncle and he needs to know where his friend is tonight, to ask if he'll join him on the Gujarat journey. 'Looking after one VIP tourist,' is the answer, when he returns.

'The Brahmin connection?' I ask and he shrugs philosophically, gesturing towards the stairs with his customary 'Shall we…?'

'But I haven't paid.'

'Nothing to pay. This much I can do,' he insists. 'You've come so far. Also…' He laughs, as he intervenes to carry my bag for me. 'In London, I think, even one Pepsi I cannot buy.'

So, at least he's worked that one out!

Two camels were waiting on a patch of bare land near the city's edge. A wiry figure in a severe army great coat stood beside them. His deeply lined face was austerely expressionless beneath a grimy yellow turban. Only the tiniest twitch of a handlebar moustache gave any sense that our cook-cum-camelman even recognised Mohamd.

Then Mohamd put me straight: this was his father. The camelman, approaching with a big bag of saucepans, was both younger and less forbidding.

'*Namaste.*' The father advanced unsmiling, his palms joined in front of him in traditional salutation; then he shook my hand to fulfil the obligations of both cultures.

'*Namaste.*' I imitated the palming-touching gesture, sensing that this would have been a greeting of few words, even if we'd had more than that one word in common. I thought of my own father, always so warmly welcoming to my friends, and asked myself how he'd relate to Mohamd. Hardly the longed-for grandson, but I knew he'd do his best. I also wondered how much Nayak senior knew about me. Mohamd had said his mother understood who I was, how I fitted in. After all, he didn't bring every tourist home for tea. But I suspected he was keeping most of his cards close to his chest and, on the whole, I hoped so. It was Mohamd I wanted to help, not the hangers-on.

The father had few more words for his son than he had for me. The encounter passed stiffly, without warmth, and I struggled to avoid a convenient pigeonholing. I couldn't help seeing this man as the source of Mohamd's problems, but that didn't make him a villain. He had a different idea of what was best for his child, but he wished it no less fervently than I did – and with greater justification!

Mohamd and I took one of the animals, while the camelman and lunch took the other. Mohamd held the long rope reigns from behind me, but once we were safely out of town, he passed them back over my head, so that I could 'steer'. He showed me how to kick with my heels to go faster, how to bounce with the trot for greater comfort.

'So you did get your father's camels,' I grunted, as I missed the rhythm and hit the saddle with a jolt. 'You must tell me what I owe him.'

'Nothing to pay,' he said firmly.

'But he's lost a day's income…'

'Oh, come on!' he scolded me with a dig in the back. 'We are not so poor.' Then he chuckled as a new thought struck him: 'Opie's going to be disappointed. He was hoping we'd get the camels through an agent, with a commission to share.'

'What's it to do with him?'

'It's normal,' said Mohamd. 'The same in shops. Thirty per cent of what you pay goes to the guide, who gives ten to the driver and ten to the local agent. But I've already told Opie – there won't be anything from Riyaz.'

'No wonder your father looked so pleased to see me!' I laughed, reflecting how generous it had been for Mohamd to forego the Riyaz commission, proving that, for him at least, things had already changed gear.

'It won't affect my parents,' he explained. 'I give them the same amount each month and save what I can. Sometimes it's difficult but, this way, if I make good business...' he chose his words carefully '...they don't have to know.'

'You have to be totally honest with me,' I told him bluntly. 'If you want me to help you.'

'I know that,' he said simply. 'I knew when you first wrote to me.'

'I still think I ought to pay your father.'

'It's not allowed,' he laughed. 'Give something to the camelman, if you like.'

'Of course, but I was hoping you'd advise me. You've no idea how hard it is for us to get it right, without looking either stupid or mean.'

Mohamd laughed sympathetically and we rode on in silence. We saw no one, only a small herd of unattended goats, stripping the few remaining leaves from a solitary, spiky-looking shrub. We heard nothing, only the camel's heavy breathing and the gentle padding of its footsteps in the stony sand. The world of the time sheet seemed immeasurably far away. I had a real sense of being healed by the *blankness* of the desert.

'You feeling maybe little bit tired?' asked Mohamd. Normally the cue for a shopping spree, this now signalled lunch at a half-ruined caravanserai. The camel obligingly knelt – first the front legs, hurling me forwards with an alarming lurch, then the back – but I had lost the use of my own legs. The thigh muscles simply wouldn't function, needing both my arms to lift a leg over the camel's back, then Mohamd's steadying hand to help me up to a nearby rooftop.

The camelman lit a campfire down below. His preparations took forever, but I didn't feel impatient. We sat in the sun. We explored what little there was to explore. And we talked. Or, for much of the time, we didn't even talk. We listened to the silence. Mohamd was proving to be one of the few people with whom I felt entirely at ease during long periods of quiet. He kept worrying that I must be bored. He couldn't understand – even I could barely understand – that this complete suspension of activity, time and purpose felt uplifting.

'How is suite?' he asked, after a while.

'The same as the old room,' I told him, 'but with two uncomfortable sofas to justify the extra charge.'

'You bring CD player?' he asked, after another interval. He'd suggested that I brought it 'to pass the time' and was keen to take a look, having never seen a Walkman. He briefly tried a couple of my Indian discs, asking disappointedly, 'You like *only* slow music?' He then rummaged through the remaining contents of my bag with an innocent, uncomplicated curiosity that felt oddly unintrusive – just a natural extension of an unexpected closeness that, it seemed, we both felt. Finding my diary, he asked if he could look up the Gujarat dates. 'Three days you spend in Bhuj,' he noted delightedly. 'And after Desert Festival! There is night bus from Jaisalmer – I think definitely we can come.'

We went to check on lunch. An hour and a half must have passed and a vegetable stew was progressing nicely. However, the water for our rice had only just been put on the fire, so we went for a stroll. 'You know Indian step well?' Mohamd asked, as we reached a pair of deep stone tanks divided by a wall. From the near side of each of them a broad flight of stairs descended into the water, as far as the algae let us see. Mohamd told me how, in summertime, the youth of Jaisalmer went there for picnics, the girls swimming on one side of the wall and the boys on the other.

The only barbecue party that he himself had attended was, however, resolutely single-sex – the presence of unmarried girls from his community being out of the question. No wonder he had so far to go in the 'playboy' stakes.

He also asked whether I knew about 'bang', which I didn't. He said it gave you good feeling, like alcohol, only better; it made you feel you could float above the ground. I assumed that it must be the local word for marijuana, but Mohamd said that it wasn't for smoking. You put it in the yoghurt drink, *lassi*. Risking fatherly wrath, he'd tried some there once and another boy, high on the mystery substance, had thrown him into the pool, which was not good news, as he couldn't swim; but fortunately Riyaz, his saviour in all things, pulled him out. I told him, when he came to England, he could visit my father who lived near the sea, where maybe we could teach him to swim. The sea was one of the many things that Mohamd had never seen.

Lunch, when finally ready, was surprisingly good, but this didn't stop Mohamd apologising for its simplicity. 'But next time, we come for two, three days,' he enthused. 'Take musicians, sleep under stars...' An idea of his for the future was to set up a desert camp for tourists who wanted to spend the night out there; a few mud huts, like the family farm; not a big investment of capital. All he needed was the driving licence. 'A new career – just like you!' he laughed.

'Except that *I* haven't found one,' I reminded him. 'But you can count me in. It sounds great.'

The camelman gave a signal that saddle-sore buttocks had to be braced for the return. 'I was asking how much?' I prompted, as Mohamd clambered on behind. 'For his tip.'

'How much you like,' he answered absent-mindedly; then, as the camels padded slowly through the dust: 'Is OK now we trot?' His idea was to hurry back to Sunset Point; but, as we approach the famous hill, with its commanding view of the city, we find that almost every tourist in Jaisalmer has had the same idea. And, predictably, every tout in the city has also come to take advantage. Young boys offer postcards, camera film, unconvincing fake editions of popular books on their country… but no fossils. 'Could one of them be Pepsi?' I wonder, searching their faces for a dazzling smile.

We squeeze ourselves on to one of the *chattris*, erected as cenotaphs for deceased Maharajas. The sun is already glowing red, but has barely moved before a police jeep draws up in the distance. Within seconds, Mohamd has darted back down to where we left the camels, insisting that I stay behind. There is no time to tell him that I'd rather see the sunset from there, or not see it at all, if that is the price of his company. Now, if I don't sit it out until the sun disappears, he'll think he's failed me; so, raging quietly at the constabulary, I pretend to be selfish in order to be kind.

'*Namaste,*' says Gajendra's uncle, pleased to see us back. Natraj and Trio are the only restaurants that Mohamd knows, but I liked it here and, in any case, neither of us is hungry. Supper is simply the framework for our last evening.

'*Namaste,*' I return the proprietor's greeting, realising stupidly late that I've been wasting the perfect opportunity to learn some Hindi. Gamely, Mohamd tries to rectify the situation, teaching me '*dhanya vad*' (thank you), '*bhot achha khana tha*' (the food was very good) and – at my request – '*mere paass nahin hai*' (I have no pens). However, the sounds are impossible to grasp. He tries again with the aid of the paper table cloth, but I still find it difficult. Every aspect of the language is so different from the European ones that I know. Yet Mohamd has taught himself most of these.

'We must order *papad*,' he announces, marking an end to the language lesson. 'And, as you're having beer, some finger chips.' I imagined some other local speciality but finger chips turn out to be chips that you eat with your fingers. And with large quantities of tomato ketchup. Mohamd is greatly fond of both finger chips and ketchup, having no need of beer as a pretext for substantial helpings, so at least this is something he could eat in England. If indeed he ever comes.

'What's in there?' he asks, pointing to the carrier bag at my feet.

'Something for you,' I tell him. I wanted to give him a thank you present, but there was no chance to go shopping, so the bag contains Elektra's Khajuraho book. She need never know: I can easily replace it in England. And yes, of course there are a thousand things that he needs more than this, but it was something I could give without patronising.

Mohamd frowns for a moment at the message written inside. Perhaps I made it too fulsome? But no, the problem is only my handwriting. 'Your computer letters are easier,' he laughs, passing speedily on to the erotic illustrations.

There will in fact be a second gift tomorrow morning. I've decided to pay for both the driving lessons and his Jodhpur living expenses: an ability to drive would open so many opportunities for him. However, I'm planning to give him the cash in an envelope when we say goodbye, so that he won't have a chance to protest. I've not been very successful at winning economic battles in the last few days. And tonight I'm outsmarted again when he disappears, ostensibly to the cloakroom but in fact to pay the bill for the second night running. He then suggests a walk to Cottage Gallery, to say goodbye.

'Next Time You See Mumda In The London,' laughs Riyaz. I'm pleased to find that his own advice is the same as mine: if Mohamd comes to England, he should do so without trying to do any business, without taking anything to sell, just acquiring some experience. I'm less pleased to see a drawer slide open, revealing a familiar pair of miniature pictures.

'They're very beautiful but I can't afford them,' I insist.

'Which One You Like The Best?' asks Riyaz undeterred, as Mohamd disappears – a sure sign that things are getting serious. 'This I Give You, Sir. Other One, No Need to Buy. Just I Show My Respect For Your Great Love Of The Art. And For All What You Do For The Mumda.' I feel embarrassed, yet he's very persistent, as only Riyaz can be persistent. In the end I accept, but feel obliged to spend on the other one.

Mohamd, returning, asks something of Riyaz, then pulls a white embroidered shawl from a shelf. 'My present for you,' he mutters shyly.

'It's beautiful,' I mumble unconvincingly. The shawl would look effeminate on Elektra, let alone me, but it was plainly all he could think of on the spur of the moment, and the thought counts powerfully.

I am more than usually bleary-eyed. Opie has insisted on an early start: the journey to Jodhpur is a long one and we need to allow time for the carpet man. So, blinking my way through reception, I don't at first notice Mohamd, looking thinner than ever in narrow-cut, pale blue jeans and matching jacket. 'More modern,' he says with forced cheeriness, as I give him the envelope containing the money.

He looks puzzled, but I explain that it's polite in England to write a letter of thanks in return for hospitality – I'm simply delivering mine by hand. He looks even more puzzled, but nods sombrely. He says he'll do his best to get to Gujarat, but privately I know this is hopelessly unrealistic.

I wonder sadly when we *shall* meet again. I really shouldn't be leaving yet. There's too much unfinished business. He deserves better. And I can't even find a way of telling him these things.

Instead, clasping his hand in both of mine, I manage to thank him in Hindi and take his appreciative laugh away with me.

'Back into normal, sir,' chuckles Opie, steering contentedly out of the city. The last few days have given *him* a break, as well as me. The car looks especially clean and he's found a sprucer shirt. He is, of course, as talkative as ever, as he tries to catch up on my movements – especially the movements of my credit card.

'Any shopping?' he asks innocently.

Five

It crosses my mind to say 'Nothing', but there will doubtless come a time when the carpet no longer fits in my luggage, so I confess to 'One small durry'; then quickly emphasise that it came from Riyaz, so as not to raise Opie's hopes.

'So, no more this Jodhpur?' he asks, now doubly disappointed.

'We'll still visit Roopraj,' I assure him. 'The one from Riyaz was sort of extra.'

'How much you pay?' He uses the special tone, which they must all learn at driving school, suggesting earnest concern that the client has not been overcharged, but in reality indicating a commission calculation in progress. Except that, on this occasion, there's nothing for Mohamd to share. Without thinking, I admit that the carpet cost much more than Roopraj's products. I must definitely keep quiet about the pictures. 'How much these your camels, sir?' This time 'Nothing' is the only possible answer and, for a moment, he looks glummer than ever; then suddenly more purposeful: 'How many carpets you buy in Jodhpur?' I explain that I have a specific and limited objective. Last year there were two identical rugs, of which I bought one. As soon as I got it home, I knew I should have bought the pair, so on this visit I am simply looking for a duplicate.

Opie makes no comment, turning instead to his sleeping arrangements. 'Which place you stay?' he asks warily. Four nights in Jaisalmer meant four payments for lodgings, so another city must be less than ideal.

'Somewhere not too expensive,' I tell him. Remarkably, I haven't even thought about it.

'This Jodhpur very expensive,' he advises. 'I know good place other side. All are these tourists liking. Same like Dariawad, only no flying squirrel.' I reach for a guidebook, but he leaps in defensively. 'Not in book, sir, new place... Old place made new,' he corrects himself, in case I pictured something brashly modern. 'Chanwa Fort they are calling.'

I agree to risk it. Then later, braving lunch in another Opie favourite, I start to have misgivings. The restaurant comprises two plastic chairs on a little patch of dried up lawn on the Jodhpur bypass. Opie recommends that I sit on the cleaner of the chairs and use the other as a table. The slowness of the kitchens beats all previous records. Three dishes that I thought might work well in combination arrive at eccentrically spaced intervals, carried by two small boys who peer at me with ill-concealed amusement. My mime of a diner using knife and fork produces giggles but no cutlery. Yet the food is good and I try to say so in my few words of Hindi, which disappointingly reduces them to hysterics.

There is no need of Hindi with Roopraj Prajapati. He is the frontman for a substantial village co-operative. It is he who has the linguistic fluency, the energy, the charm – not to mention the credit card machine – to make an unpromising dusty courtyard the best-known carpet-making enterprise in Rajasthan. He not only recognises me but also enquires after Andrew. 'Your friend, he buy one green carpet, you one red,' he remembers accurately. I explain my need of a duplicate but there is nothing remotely similar. 'This also red,' he advises. For all his virtues, Roopraj is slow to grasp the concept of a pair. However, fortunately I have a photo in my luggage.

'Twelve weeks, same, same, I send to England,' Roopraj promises.

'Success!' cries Opie, looking delighted, even though I'm leaving empty-handed. Roopraj's assistant must have briefed him on my purchase and, for once, he doesn't even ask the price. The jaunty whistling says he knows already.

'Does Chanwa Fort have telephones? I ask, as we drive away. 'I need to contact the Gujarat guide.' My heart sinks as I say this. Life is about to become regimented but, for Andrew, coming all this way for a week, every day needs to count. Also, none of the Delhi drivers speaks Gujarati, so Mahtani said we had to have a guide, if only to act as an interpreter; and Sheikh, who showed us round Udaipur, was at least someone we liked. Yet I still feel sad to be losing my liberty.

'I know this guide,' says Opie, pulling off the road beside a minuscule PCO-STD-ISD.

'I know him too,' I protest, as Opie squeezes in beside me and starts to dial the number. I'd like Sheikh's advice on an Udaipur hotel. I want something simple this time, something in the heart of the old town, not the rarefied palace in the middle of the lake, where we stayed before.

'Leave all to me,' says Opie, when the number fails to answer. 'First to Chanwa, then later this Sheikh I am calling.'

The Fort is delightful – all delicate, pink sandstone, dotted with elegant balconies and jali-work. The style implies a period of peace and prosperity, but the receptionist has no idea which. 'All writ in room,' he promises and sure enough, at the back of a drawer, I find a brief information sheet, stating that the nineteenth century builder was both a minister and poet laureate to the Jodhpur Maharaja. He was also something called a 'Charan', but the boy who brings my bags shakes his head: 'Sorry, sir. Not know this word.'

In the dining room, a dignified, middle-aged man comes to introduce himself as the owner. 'Are you descended from the poet?' I ask him, but he shakes his head.

'I'm the uncle of the present Maharaja. When the poet died without an heir, the Fort reverted to the Crown.'

'And he was a… what was it… 'Charan'?'

'Absolutely.'

I was hoping for more, but my host needs to circulate.

'Mind if my wife and I join you?' asks another guest, unable to find a free table. 'Actually, there'll be three of us. Our guide, you know. Charming chap but, after a fortnight…' His wife digs him in the ribs. She, like me, has noticed the gleaming white teeth of a familiar smile bearing down on us.

'Mr Moon, sir, I am being very surprised!' exclaims the newcomer. 'You are looking ten years more young!' Sharma the Charmer has lost none of his charm and his charges listen contentedly, as our brief shared history takes the conversational pressure off them. 'You remember that time that your plane was six hours late?'

'Everyone else seemed to know about it,' I laugh.

'The airport deserted,' he chuckles nostalgically, pausing briefly to waive aside a meat dish. 'I am being Brahmin,' he reminds us, as we exchange knowing glances, each tempted to sing along with the well-remembered patter: 'Brahmins highest caste: priests. But I am not priest…'

'Is there a "guiding caste"?' I manage to interrupt him.

'Oh no, sir.' He laughs at my ignorance. 'Guiding, driving, agenting… All these are new jobs.'

'Does that mean you can change your caste?... Rise above it?... Through education, for instance?'

'Oh no, sir.' Mr Sharma shakes his head, incredulous that I should still be asking such things. 'With education we can be finding better job, making money. But always we are having same caste.'

'Or through marrriage? Suppose a farming girl marries a prince…?'

'A farming girl is marrying a farmer, sir.'

'Yes, that's what I thought you'd say. So what caste are Charans?'

'These are special caste,' he answers, only momentarily disoriented. 'Bards, sir. Poets to the Rajput community, glorificating their achievements, spurring them on to battle… Very much prestigious persons. Even today, they are getting top jobs normally given to Brahmins and Rajputs.'

'And what about the Nayak caste?'

Mr Sharma thinks for a moment, clearly puzzled at my non-sequitur. 'These are some low-caste persons,' he answers vaguely. 'These are horse-breeders, camel-breeders… Nothing to do with Fort Chanwa.'

'No good hotel before Udaipur,' says Opie, disappointed to see my packed bags. 'Better two nights Fort Chanwa.'

'I'm making a detour,' I tell him. 'Somewhere Mr Sharma recommended. I looked it up on the map.'

'Which place?' he asks suspiciously. The atlas has caused enough trouble already.

'Narlai,' I venture, expecting resistance.

'Oh, this very good place.' With even better drivers' facilities to judge from his enthusiastic loading of my cases.

'What's happening in that school?' I ask in the first town we come to. The pupils are massed in serried ranks, like soldiers except that they are sitting cross-legged and have just completed a sequence of synchronised arm exercises to general applause.

'Republic Day,' says Opie, reluctantly stopping.

I peer round the gate and am instantly spotted by the man in the middle of the row of teachers on a platform. I make to withdraw but he beckons me up the steps and a junior teacher makes his seat available. The man whom I take to be the headmaster asks the usual questions concerning my name, country name and occupation, while the children and the token group of parents at the edge of the playground talk among themselves; then he activates a crackly microphone. 'We shall now proceed to the giving of the prizes,' he announces self-importantly. 'Today we have a distinguished visitor, most important London lawyer.' (I still don't know what else to say.) 'We are very happy that he is going to distribute.' He passes me a bundle of pencils, whispering, 'One each,' as a long list of names is called. 'Finally, top prize for Student of the Year.' He hands me a single plastic biro. 'Now all clap hands for illustrious guest.'

The shade beneath Narlai's bougainvillaea looked enticing and an outdoor bed, piled with cushions, invited an afternoon of indolent slumber. However, I was no sooner settled than a tall, wiry figure with enormous eyes and the biggest, reddest turban that I've ever seen proposed a stroll. It takes me a moment to realise that he must be one of the waiters. Reading my hesitation as a failure to understand, he started to act out the concept of a walk with exaggerated pantomime gestures and a huge zany grin. It seemed prudent to humour him but, as he leads me in and out of uncomplaining villagers' houses, the grimaces and gesticulations grow more outlandish still.

I realise how much I miss Mohamd. In Jaisalmer, I had a close-up view that made me feel involved. Here, for all this eccentric's good intentions, the gauze has descended again. I'm seeing things more hazily, from a distance.

'Where is wife?' my companion asks abruptly, pulling a face of overstated puzzlement.

'No wife,' I reply and brace myself for the reaction. I have already seen him act out several human emotions, but surprise is one that he does most immoderately.

'*NO WIFE???*' he gasps, eyes rolling and body reeling.

'Too expensive,' I explain, as the stock evasion pulls him back from the brink.

Opie refuses to say what Udaipur hotel arrangements have been made. 'It's a surprise,' he tells me with a wink.

Determined to play the guide, he has spent the whole morning finding views for me to photograph, spotting birds for me to admire, uncovering facts with which to astound me. He is also more than usually keen to catalogue his own incomparable qualities, reminding me how clever he was to repair the clutch that night, emphasising that he'd never have taken that wrong turning outside Bikaner, if he hadn't been so worried about his wife… It can only be our imminent link-up with Sheikh that has precipitated this wave of insecurity.

He does, however, have another surprise for me. 'How far your home from this Swindon?' he asks, producing a dog-eared envelope from his trouser pocket. 'One English girl travel with me last year. She write me many times.' As close as Opie will ever get to shy, he hands me the letter in its envelope. 'I have present,' he continues more urgently. 'Is possible you can take for me?'

'About a hundred kilometres,' I estimate, resigning myself to a wasted Saturday.

'Oh,' he answers, apparently judging this too great a distance to impose on me, and we say no more on the subject. I feel little sympathy for his holiday romance but, in any case, I'm much more interested in the envelope, addressed to Omprakash Yadav.

The penny has dropped: Omprakash Yadav… **Om P**rakash… **O.P.**… Of course! Not *Opie* at all. But it is too late now. I have travelled too far with 'Opie' to make the rest of the journey with 'O.P.'

I had forgotten that Sheikh ran a travel agency, in addition to his guiding work. 'The Voice of Trade and Travel' proclaims the painted signboard, only slightly shabbier for another two years' wear and tear; and, when Opie sounds his horn, Sheikh sprints out to greet me. 'Hundred per cent welcome, sir,' he enthuses, in his husky, warm voice. Exactly as I remember him, he wears a shirt and tie under a grey v-necked pullover, with his distinctive cloth cap. He is older than Mohamd, indeed older than me, I should think, and a wise and tolerant man, I've always felt. 'Hotel as per your wishes, sir. Maximum persons they like for view, but possible backpackers in cheaper rooms…'

The narrowness of the alley leading down to the Caravanserai suggests that motorised arrivals might be rare, but Opie is determined to prove it can be done. Meanwhile, Sheikh is anxious to stress how hard he negotiated to secure the best room.

'Number 31?' says the man on the desk.

'Hundred per cent,' Sheikh confirms, explaining to the receptionist that I am one of the UK's leading solicitors. (He has never spared the hyperbole, if it reflects a little glory on himself.) Then he insists on accompanying me up three flights of stairs, so it is hard to mask my disappointment on entering the room. 'Spartan' would be the kindest description: no furniture beyond a large double bed, some shelves and a hanging rail for my clothes. The marble floor is hard and cold and the bathroom the sort where the shower will soak everything, including the towels, as soon as the taps are turned. Only when Sheikh pulls back the curtains, do I see the point. We're at the corner of the building, with huge picture windows filling two sides of the room: in one direction, an imposing view of the City Palace; in the other, a close-up of the lake.

Sheikh excuses himself hastily: he has a Diplomatic party to escort on a sunset cruise, with tomorrow committed to the President of a big multi-national. (Even in my heyday, I was one of his humbler clients.) He'll come to see me off in a couple of days, then meet me down in Ahmedabad on Friday night. However, I hardly pay attention. The sunlight streaming down a fourth flight of stairs is drawing me up to a rooftop restaurant, where I quickly set about filming the panoramic view.

'Look at that for a video,' says a friendly Welsh voice from behind me. 'Never seen one so small!'

'Bet he's got all sorts of fancy apparatus!' chuckles her partner, with a similar regional lilt.

'Bet it was him in that car,' the woman continues teasing.

'Course it was. Didn't you see the swanky chauffeur?'

'Bet he's on the expensive top floor!'

'Bet he's got matching luggage and all!'

I pray they never see that I have, but the good-natured leg-pulling sucks me into their circle. They are teachers from Wales, Linda and Huw, taking early retirement to backpack around India (Sheikh forgot to mention that the backpackers might be in their fifties!) and in no time they've drawn me out on the subject of my own extended time here.

'So what next?' demands Linda. 'You can't retire. You're younger than us!'

'I don't really have any plans. I'm just juggling ideas...'

'Sorry for disturb,' a waiter breaks in. 'Guide is in reception.'

'Told you he'd have a guide,' laughs Huw, as I make for the stairs. 'Anyway don't be long,' he calls after me. 'I'm ordering you a beer.'

'You're sure this Friday night meet-up is OK?' says Sheikh, jumping up. 'You see, Thursday night I must be here for Eid Festival, end of Ramadan. My daughter, she is coming from the Delhi...' It never occurred to me that he'd do other than meet me in Ahmedabad so, as soon as I can get a word in, I agree. 'After the Gujarat, sir, hundred per cent I return with you. First stop, I think, Zainabad, simple desert camp...' Without listening to the detail, I resign myself to more chaperoned activity.

'Your beer's getting warm,' says Huw, as I return to the terrace. 'But you were telling us about your plans.'

'Lack of plans,' I remind him. 'Just ideas... Perhaps a non-executive directorship...' Linda pulls a face. 'Or help run a charity...' She looks more equivocal. 'Maybe the wine trade, even something in the theatre...'

'Meet Renaissance Man!' mocks Huw.

'I didn't say I was good at any of this! But I've always hated having to specialise, even at school. Yet what did I do as a lawyer? Focussed ever more restrictively on a tiny area, ending up one of those people who are famous for knowing all there is to know about very little!'

'Don't worry, you'll forget it all soon enough,' laughs Linda, nudging Huw to remind him that it's time for them to leave me. They are going to the Lake Palace for dinner tonight. They have only T-shirts and track suit bottoms and will be despised. In a different time, I might have despised them too. Now I wish I were going with them.

'Morning, Professor,' teases Linda, spotting the Rajput architecture book, as I join them for breakfast. 'Homework for the City Palace?' she guesses correctly. 'We only do the India Handbook at this table. Not that we're doing anything cultural today. We're hiring bikes to go round the other lake. Wouldn't suit you,' she laughs, little knowing how I envy them. 'But tomorrow morning we're going upmarket. More your sort of day...'

'Splashing out on a taxi,' boasts Huw. 'Up to the Monsoon Palace for the sunrise.' I doubt that anyone has ever got more out of Udaipur than these two.

'Listen,' says Linda, flicking idly through the glossary in her guidebook. 'Is a "Kattakat" : (a) an Orissan temple hall with a pyramid roof, (b) a Gujarati dish made of liver, kidney and brains or (c) a Himalayan blue sheep?'

'Err, the temple thing?'

'Wrong! It's the offal. You did say you were going to Gujarat didn't you?'

Long after I intended to be at the City Palace, I am still playing 'Call My Bluff' in the sunshine. It's a long time since I've laughed so much. When they finally remember the bicycles, I take a meandering back street route, getting happily lost in the tangle of alleyways near the ghats, so it's almost lunchtime when I reach the palace ticket booth. 'This afternoon,' I promise myself but, a beer and a sandwich later, I've changed my mind. It can wait till after Gujarat. A good excuse to come back. The more pressing question is whether I can stir myself into painting action. The lake looks a daunting subject, but my sketch from the rooftop goes better than I hoped. Even the paint is flowing well when the cyclists return.

'Look, more ritzy gadgetry!' Linda points to the painting stool. 'Surprised he hasn't got an easel!' (Thank goodness I left that in my room.)

'Is it anywhere we know?' asks Huw, pretending not to recognise my interpretation of the lake.

Despite the ribbing, I have nearly finished, when the waiter announces that my guide is back in reception.

'Sir, I've been thinking,' says Sheikh. 'Maybe better I travel with you. The Eid, I think, is coming too late. It depends on new moon. We must celebrate next day and maximum persons they now think Friday night. But by then, you must be in the Ahmedabad already, for Mr Andrew Saturday morning.'

'Whatever you think best,' I cut him off impatiently.

'Sir, I am also thinking, good place on the way will be Dungarpur, the Udai Bilas Palace…' My week with him is fast becoming a fortnight, but I meekly authorise the booking. 'Also in

Dungarpur there is great healer. Maximum tourists, they don't see. Using no medicine, not even herbal medicine, only faith.'

'I'd better think of something wrong with me,' I jest, as I try to get away, then see from his frown that jesting isn't appropriate. 'My sister does have an illness,' I volunteer, to compensate. 'She has multiple sclerosis.'

Sheikh frowns again, as if he's never heard of it, but with a cheery 'Hundred per cent we go and ask,' he releases me.

'We've ordered for three,' says Linda, by way of indication that I'm joining them for dinner. However, they need an early night so, as soon as we have finished, I set off alone for the promontory jutting out into the lake. It formed the centre of my painting, but I've never explored it before.

The poorly lit streets are much less visited than those near the hotel. The ever-present 'art students' make only the most desultory efforts to sell me paintings and I can sit undisturbed on some steps leading down to the water, enjoying the reflected lights of my hotel. Then a youthful figure slinks from the shadows.

'First time in Udaipur?' he asks, approaching slowly through a pool of light that draws attention to the tightness of his jeans and T-shirt.

'Second,' I answer, as he sits unexpectedly close.

'I see you before,' he informs me and I turn for a better view of the finely chiselled features and well-cut hair, wondering when we might have seen each other. 'You are coming alone?' he asks softly.

'This time, yes,' I mumble, thinking it might look gauche to inch away.

'I am art student.' He fixes me with the full force of a garlicky smile. 'Please, you come to my school.' He puts a hand lightly on my knee. 'We have coffee and talk.'

In any other country, this would all signal 'rent'. Here, for all the flirtatious charm, I'm sure it's only art, not flesh, that's for sale, but I am not in the market for either. 'I'm here to *paint,* not to *buy* pictures,' I tell him primly.

'I'm always here, if you change your mind,' he says with a wink. Then, as he shakes my hand, a finger tickles my palm, leaving less room for doubt as to what it is that I've declined.

'Wait till you see this in daylight,' says Sheikh in the darkness of the Udai Bilas courtyard, and I restrain myself from observing that we could have seen it this afternoon, but for him.

The journey need not have been a long one, but it started with a major diversion: Sheikh was determined to take me somewhere special for lunch and, when the 'somewhere special' turned out to be Dariawad, I knew that he'd been got at by Opie. The best thing about the place was the prospect of a solitary (as Sheikh was observing Ramadan) lunch in the garden; but a swarm of flies quickly put an end to that. And in the claustrophobic dining room, the owner and a fasting Sheikh spent the whole of the meal, not to mention the long delay while it was prepared, having an interminable conversation in Hindi. It was like being a child again, seen but not heard. 'You're not bored?' asked Sheikh, after an hour and a half of this. It was not a good start.

'Sorry, sir, we were expecting you this afternoon,' says a figure, emerging from the gloom. 'But wait till you see this in daylight.' Even in the dark, I can see that Dungarpur's palace is one of the most remarkable buildings that I've ever set eyes on, let alone spent the night in; and they've upgraded me to a suite of three rooms, the most spectacular of which has both a ceiling and a floor made of mirrors. Sheikh beams with satisfaction, as if it were all thanks to him.

Down by the lakeside, a small cocktail party is underway, lit by candles floating on the water. 'Welcome to the Dungarpur Fan Club!' says a glamorous Indian woman. She introduces herself as

Royina and asks me about my travels, about the story that lies behind my Indian winter, adding that her husband gave up a Bombay banking career to run a farm… *Of course!* I thought her name was familiar… *Royina Grewal!* She wrote that book I was reading about a different journey to Jaisalmer… And now she's asking me what comes next.

Although I answer this question almost every day, I'm more than usually hesitant tonight and this is because an entirely new idea is taking shape.

'I might write a book.'

I pause, expecting doubts, even outright derision, but Royina merely looks politely interested to know more.

'A book about Rajasthan… but not like yours.' I feel flustered, more than a little in awe. I've never met anyone who talks in such perfect sentences, paragraphs even; but I plough on incoherently. 'A particular *aspect* of Rajasthan. You see, I've been spending a lot of my time in these amazing palaces, but I sit there in the evenings thinking, I don't know where I am. I don't know who lived here. I don't *even* know which century it belongs to. And there's nothing in print to tell me.'

'You're right about the gap in the market,' she says encouragingly. 'Just one or two things that *touch* on this area. I can send you a bibliography.'

I take this as a seal of approval and add the idea to my shortlist of possible futures.

'Where's Sheikh?' I demand of Opie. I'm scheduled to visit an abandoned thirteenth century palace: the one occasion when Sheikh could have justified his presence and he chooses it to go missing! Opie mumbles something to the effect that the moon popped up last night, so the Eid is today and my guide is at the Mosque. I must make do with Mr Yadav.

'This monkey.' He points to a fresco of Hanuman. 'This elephant.' He indicates Ganesh, then scratches his groin in search of further inspiration. 'Come, sir…' He beckons me to a small, dark niche containing some more than usually red-blooded scenes from the Karma Sutra. 'You like?' he gurgles with a ladish nudge. My polite amusement seems less than he was hoping for, so he tries his luck with a middle-aged couple: 'Madam, sir, you like see naughty cupboard?' For a while he becomes *their* guide, leaving me to amble round peacefully, and I note from a distance how much more comfortable he seems with them. Indeed the wife, perhaps unhinged by the medieval pornography, seems oddly charmed by Opie, even reluctant to release him, when it is time to find Sheikh for our appointment with the faith healer.

A team of acolytes is busy, herding the sick into orderly lines, but Sheikh and I are ushered straight to sit cross-legged at the front. The Mullahna's speciality, Sheikh explains, is the removal of kidney stones, but with none of the bother of surgery. Each patient brings an X-ray, which the healer briefly studies to locate the stone. Then he makes what appears to be a symbolic surgical cut across the patient's bare abdomen, before pulling the clothing back down and putting a hand underneath, next tugging firmly and unclenching his fist to reveal the offending stone. There is more than a touch of 'nothing up my sleeve' about it all, yet I am well within touching distance and can see no obvious trickery. Moreover, Sheikh says the patients are encouraged to go back to their conventional doctors to check that the cure has been successful, so presumably it must be, or the next wave of sufferers would take more convincing.

Having worked his way through the throng, the Mullahna comes to talk to us. He radiates goodness, yet still I feel uncomfortable: I'm not at all sure why I'm here. Perhaps Sheikh provides the answer, when he broaches the subject of my sister.

Multiple sclerosis will be quite a challenge, the Mullahna admits, especially from a distance, but he is cautiously optimistic. My sister should wait until after her next period, then bathe, wear a new bra for a couple of days and send it to him to meditate over. I find myself writing all this down, even noting all his contact details, wondering how I shall ever explain this to my disabled sister.

'Isn't it time we left for Ahmedabad?' I ask, but the one o'clock prayer drowns me out and Sheikh is announcing that he is off to the Mosque again. 'Only half an hour,' he promises. 'Maximum guests they like to visit bazaar...'

As it happens, I was longing to do precisely that, but feel that I might have been consulted.

'You said half an hour,' I remind him acerbically, when he returns nearly an hour late, but he's on such a high that it seems to pass him by and I immerse myself moodily in the backseat library. A few minutes later, he squeezes my arm apologetically.

'Hundred per cent we'll be in Ahmedabad by dinner time, sir. Maybe little *late* dinner time, but tomorrow morning you can rest, while I go to airport...'

I'm hardly listening, because one of my books has just uncovered a gem. I've never given much thought to the question of Opie's social standing, merely vaguely assuming that he slotted in somewhere lower down the scale from Mohamd's Mark Two Rajputs – even if they *were* given to camel-breeding. But the book says the Yadavs were medieval kings! And for all the lack of regal graces in their latter-day descendant, I'm sure that the point wasn't lost on the young Mr Nayak. Because that's how the system seems to work. It doesn't matter how much you spit and belch and scratch your balls: it doesn't tarnish your status.

Six

I felt apprehensive about Andrew's arrival: my pottering pace would surely clash with his own more exacting expectations. I also felt ashamed not to be there at the airport, instead of lingering in the calm of the hotel; even more ashamed when he walked in with Sheikh, before I'd paid my bill. 'Useless dropout,' he probably thought, but didn't say so.

'You've lost weight,' he noted. 'And you've lost that grey look from the city.' He looked different himself. Still city-grey, but somehow more youthful, less severe. Then I worked it out: he'd switched to contact lenses. 'Daft time to change,' he admitted. 'I'll only lose them in the desert. But you're not the only one entitled to a new lease of life! Anyway...' he turned purposefully to Sheikh. 'What's lined up for today?'

'Sir, first we visit textile museum...' Andrew flashed me a doubtful look. 'Next, one archaeological excavation...' Andrew looked even less convinced. 'Mahtani's programme,' Sheikh countered defensively.

'We should have gone straight to the hotel,' Andrew grumbled at the end of the afternoon. 'At least you could have told me what you've been up to, what I've been missing. Not to mention... *how was it you put it?...* "who you've turned out to be". You never said much on the phone.'

'Over dinner,' I promised.

However, our dinner table is laid for three: Sheikh is dining with us. And perhaps he's simply tired, like the two of us, but tonight he's unusually argumentative – especially when Andrew asks after Mohamd, which means explaining the offer to help, and this plainly doesn't find favour.

'He's jealous,' says Andrew, back in our room.

'I'm sure it's not that. It's the fact that we're singling someone out.'

'It's none of his business.'

'We knew he had a mind of his own. It's partly why we liked him... But you don't think he'll be difficult in Bhuj?'

'With Mohamd?' Andrew laughs for the first time all day. 'He'll never come! You've forgotten how lazy he is. And anyway, it's impossibly far for him.'

'Is this really happening?' groaned Andrew, as we entered the Alang ship-breaking yard.

'Maximum persons liking,' Sheikh assured us. 'Only problem, I think Mahtani forget this is Sunday.' And sure enough, the biggest ship-destruction centre in the world was eerily silent. Not one of the scores of vessels ranged along the shoreline was being so much as tampered with. Sheikh apologised: this would never have featured in the itinerary, if he had drawn it up himself. Nor, he emphasised, would tomorrow's three-night stay in Gondal: 'Maximum tourists stopping one night only, just to enjoy Maharaja's palace.'

This was not what I wanted to hear. It was one thing having *no* plans. I was getting comfortably used to that. But when I did have them, I didn't want to worry whether they were the right ones!

Knowing two fractious clients when he saw them, Sheikh excused himself from dinner duty. He muttered something about calling Mahtani's office, but I think even he had sensed that we might have things to talk about.

'So, tell me the worst,' Andrew jokes, as we go down to eat. 'You've decided to run away and join the circus!'

I never get a chance to confirm or deny because a packed hotel dining room forces us to share a table, putting the much-needed catch-up on hold once again. We foist ourselves apologetically on a young Indian couple and, to break the ice, I ask them, what brings them here? They don't look like ship-breaking enthusiasts.

'A cousin's marriage in the local church,' says the husband. 'The bride's from Kerala, like us, but her father runs a business here.'

'Heaven knows why he picked your cousin as a son-in-law!' the wife teases.

'So, you're Christians,' says Andrew, intrigued. 'But you still have arranged marriages?'

'Of course,' says the husband. 'Well, actually, our parents did give us *some* say…'

'They gave us a veto,' the wife interpolates. 'I kept saying "no" to everyone they came up with. It seemed safest. Then I realised, I'd end up an old maid. I persuaded myself that Thomas didn't seem quite as bad as the rest of them!' She looks at him fondly.

'So you did meet each other before the marriage?' asks Andrew, still curious.

'We had dinner together,' explains Thomas.

'Could you really decide something like that over dinner?'

'You're forgetting our parents' research,' says the wife, taking Thomas's hand. 'We knew that we shared the same background, the same values. All we had to do was make sure we could "vibe" together.'

'Whatever that means,' laughs Thomas, embarrassed.

'At last!' sighed Andrew, as we arrived at Palitana. 'Something substantial!'

'Nine hundred Jain temples,' Sheikh confirmed with satisfaction, as if he had personally made them available.

But unfortunately every one of those temples was built on a mountaintop, with four thousand steps leading up to it, and no sooner had we arrived at the summit than Sheikh started fretting that the restaurants down below might be closing, so we started back down after only twenty minutes. Not that it helped. It was mid-afternoon when we reached the bottom, by which time the only source of refreshment still trading was a shabby state hotel and the luke-warm remnants of a buffet.

At least the gloomy lighting served to ease Andrew gently into the full gothic horror of our driver's table manners. Having previously sat apart from us, Opie suddenly chose today to upgrade himself to the main party, yet he hardly said a word. He had hardly said a word since Sheikh appeared on the scene. It was somehow not his place to make the small-talk, while the guide was there. But what a false impression for Andrew!

Conversely, something in the cheerless surroundings seemed to render Sheikh more loquacious. He talked expansively about his family and about his principle anxiety: the need to find marriage partners for both his son and daughter. They were both at an age when this could hardly be delayed. 'As per his researches,' there were a couple of good families in Jodhpur, but how to set aside the time?

'Will they meet before the wedding?' asked Andrew innocently. 'We met this Keralan couple. Their marriage was arranged, but they each had a chance to say "no".'

'My children wouldn't expect that,' said Sheikh, suddenly severe and closed.

Searching for a change of subject, I spotted a boy eating alone at another table. He couldn't have been more than ten and I recounted how, in Jaisalmer, I'd seen another boy, even younger, enjoying just such a dinner for one. Incredibly, I explained, he was one of the city's most popular guides and the principal breadwinner for a large family – his parents a pair of drug addicts, incapable of supporting themselves, let alone their numerous children. Once in a while, after a particularly remunerative day, he'd treat himself.

'And what do you think of that?' asked Sheikh.

'I think it's very impressive. Not many eight year olds can support their families.'

'I think it's terrible,' said Sheikh. 'The boy should not spend that money on himself.'

'You see,' I whisper, back in the car. 'The whole weight of Indian society is ranged against us.'

'Well, we're not feeding the hungry Nayak hordes to please Sheikh,' answers Andrew.

'Leave all to me,' Sheikh had said about the three-night Gondal problem.

'Last time I do that,' says Andrew on our final afternoon. 'It's been bad enough having Sheikh with us every single minute. But waking us yesterday at 4 o'clock for a three and a half hour drive! It would have been one thing if we'd actually *seen* some lions – which I'm sure we would have done, if we hadn't made endless stops for Sheikh's *chai* – but surprise, surprise, by the time *we* roll up, anything that moves has retreated to the shade!' The expedition to the Gir safari park was not an unqualified success. 'Then what does he line up for today?' Andrew still can't believe it himself. 'A Maharaja's car collection and a *cattle breeding farm*!'

I am running out of ways of apologising. And it hasn't helped that we've been frittering away what's left of day two on my new email software. Our Maharani-turned-hotelier has invited us over to test it on her private line, but we keep getting the same old error messages. Until the telephone rings with an incoming call.

'It's for you,' says the Maharani in amazement. 'A boy from Jaisalmer.' The number I gave to Mohamd turns out to be the hotline to the throne and the good news is that he and Gajendra ARE coming to Bhuj.

'Or *is* it good news?' I ask myself, still uneasy about how they'll fit in.

'Where are they going to stay?' asks Andrew.

'I didn't ask,' I answer irritably. 'It's the least of my worries. Anyway, our own place sounds pretty basic.'

'Don't depress me!' groans Andrew. 'You did *read* this itinerary, when you booked it, I suppose?' Then more brightly: 'But fancy Mohamd coming all that way! Perhaps he really will make it to England. You said he seemed keen?'

'He feels it's important to achieve something in the West.'

'Like what?' Andrew laughs.

'I don't know. It's not for us to prejudge. But he thinks it might liberate him, empower him…' Andrew laughs again, more dismissively. It sounded more convincing the way Mohamd put it.

'Can't we go straight to the hotel?' protested Andrew. The drive to Bhuj had been exhausting enough without a visit to Indian Airlines. And anyway, the boys might be there by now.

'Maximum times we go to confirm,' insisted Sheikh. And just as well that we did. It gave us useful notice that the Sunday evening flight, for which Andrew held a ticket, was non-existent. It wasn't a cancellation: the plane from Bhuj to Bombay had never been scheduled. He could fly from Bhuj tomorrow, cutting a short holiday even shorter. He could fly on Monday, but miss an important work meeting. The least of all available evils was a four o'clock start on Sunday morning for a five-hour drive to Rajkot airport, then a wasted half-day in Bombay.

It was time to lay down a few laws. Law one: Mahtani must organise a fast and comfortable car. Law two: he must pay for a first rate Bombay hotel. I was all set to call the man directly, but

Sheikh preferred to diffuse things. 'Leave all to me,' he advised. 'All will be fine.'

'It had better be. Remember, we're lawyers.' (I still was, when it suited me.)

We knew the safari lodge would be simple. What Mahtani hadn't prepared us for was the solid wooden beds, almost harder than the floor; or the desolate, dried-up garden, almost bleaker than the surrounding desert. We looked round hopefully for Mohamd and Gajendra. Perhaps it had all been all too difficult.

'Any message?' I asked the manager, fearing the worst.

'Oh yes', he answered casually. 'Two Rajasthani boys came looking for you. They said they'd come back.' And indeed, we have hardly reached our room before the boys come waving and grinning up the path.

It's the baseball-capped stranger who surges more confidently ahead, accepting a beer, while Mohamd orders Pepsi; asking animatedly after our tour, while Mohamd sits tongue-tied. Gajendra looks less boyish, more thickset; better fed and better paid perhaps. Certainly the camera slung on his shoulder looks more expensive than Mohamd could afford. He shows a robust, sardonic sense of humour, which we readily relate to; yet, for all our protests, he finds it even harder than his friend to suppress the 'sirs'.

Getting to Bhuj meant an eighteen-hour overnight bus (and anyone familiar with even the *outside* of Indian buses knows there are very few comparable tortures). They quickly chose the cheapest hotel they could find and hired an auto-rickshaw for the fourteen-kilometre journey out from the city, only to be sent rudely away by our proprietor, who refused to believe that we knew them. Then they walked back to the road to wait two hours for a bus and were just entering Bhuj when they spotted us, choosing that very

118

moment to leave, so they came all the way back here in another rickshaw. 'But really, sir, it was no problem,' says Gajendra. 'We had nothing else to do.'

'Was the owner OK with you this time?' I ask. 'We haven't met him yet.'

They exchange glances, uncertain how much to tell us. 'He thought we'd come to sell you something.' Gajendra chuckles at the improbability of the idea. 'But what's your programme here in Bhuj?'

'Two days of jeep excursions, visiting tribal villages,' I tell him, acutely conscious how unsuitable all this is for them. 'But we could always do something different…'

'We come for the pleasure to see you,' says Gajendra, looking to his friend for endorsement, but Mohamd is puzzling over Andrew's lack of spectacles.

'We saw one time in movie,' Mohamd enthuses, when Andrew explains about his contact lenses. 'That time we go to Jodhpur.'

The exchange is trivial, yet it says much about the way in which their view of the world is pieced together from accidental scraps of experience, underlining their thirst for almost anything beyond the narrow confines that they know. And as if he were thinking the same, Mohamd suddenly flourishes his passport. It came sooner than expected.

'Look at the photo,' chuckles Gajendra. 'He looks sixteen.'

'Surely fifteen.' I join in the joke, thinking privately that what the photograph really makes him look is utterly raring to get to an airport.

'I've brought the visa forms,' says Andrew, as the manager arrives with our drinks. We venture the suggestion of a dinner for four and, surprisingly, this is no problem, nor is a foursome in the jeep, nor even the notion of the manager seeking out Opie to put him on standby to drive the boys into Bhuj. So all seems fine…

Until Andrew discovers (the hard way) the lack of hot water in the shower, so I set off in search of the manager again. There's no hot water system as such, he explains: a fire has to be lit beneath our water tank, but he'll send someone to do this, so everything's fine again. But then I meet Sheikh, looking worried.

He hasn't, as he hoped, been offered accommodation here, so he'll be looking in town... Well, so be it. I don't mind where he sleeps. I just want my own shower... But, no, Sheikh has more important news. 'Sir, I am sorry,' he begins hesitantly. 'You see, there is some problem with the Opie. Somehow he has taken against the boys. I don't know why but he says he won't take them into Bhuj.'

'He's paid to be my driver. He'll take me or my friends where I tell him.'

'Sir, I explain these things, but he says, no, they are not coming in his car.'

'We'll see about that...'

I find Opie pacing moodily near the kitchens. 'I have no problem, sir,' he mumbles, but his sulky stance makes it clear that he has.

'Mr Sheikh says you have a problem with taking the boys back to Bhuj.'

'No, sir.'

'You're sure? Because the boys are my guests. If you refuse to take them, it's the same as if you refuse to take me.'

'You want the boys they come in this my car, I take them.'

Well, that seems to be settled, but he still looks glum. I tell him about his two days off, while we take the jeep, but he looks grumpier still. In a final effort to cheer him up, I offer a 'special whisky' when he gets back from Bhuj. 'He's being ridiculous,' is the angry verdict at the cottage. 'And as for your peace offering...!' Andrew thinks I've been equally ridiculous, but *he* doesn't have to live with Opie for the rest of the winter.

A table has been laid for us indoors, next to the kitchen, presumably so that the serving boys can slouch across the shortest possible distance. We ask to eat in the open and, unwillingly, they fling a food-stained cloth over an outside table. As the tepid food arrives, an overweight, sour-looking Indian appears beside us. 'Mike,' he says improbably, offering a perfunctory handshake. 'My manager says you want these boys in the jeep.'

'He said it was no problem.'

'I own this place and my jeep is not for these boys.'

'They're our friends. They've come a long way to see us.'

'It doesn't matter,' Mohamd intervenes. 'We've seen you tonight. Perhaps we can meet tomorrow evening.'

'That's ridiculous. After all that you've put yourselves through…'

'You'll have to go in your car,' says Mike.

'But Mahtani said the most interesting villages were inaccessible by car. And we've just given the driver two days off.'

'I'm not telling you again.' Mike starts to turn his back. 'My jeep is not for your so-called friends. Not for boys from Jaisalmer!'

'You're a racist!' shouts Andrew and for a moment I think Mike may be about to hit him. Instead, he merely curls his lip in a mocking smile and suggests that we finish our meal.

Mohamd and Gajendra make a valiant effort to get the evening's shipwrecked conversation back afloat, but I am literally shaking with anger. 'You're spoiling their evening,' Andrew whispers. 'They're embarrassed.' I know. But I can't help it. I wanted to give Mohamd the best of welcomes. There was no treat that I wouldn't have given him tonight, yet all we've offered is this disgusting meal in the worst hotel I've ever stayed in, where everyone from the management to my driver seems intent on being foul to him.

Eventually the manager returns with a compromise: instead of taking two of us twice, the jeep will take four of us once. We'll have to revert to our car on the second day; but that's fine, says Mohamd. By then, he and Goppu, as he calls his friend, will have had to set off home.

I suggest finding Opie, but Andrew wants to go through the visa application. He has already completed most of the blanks. Mohamd merely needs to fill in the personal data, then it can be posted. 'Riyaz say I must take all to Delhi,' says Mohamd, reluctant to concentrate.

'The post is fine,' says Andrew, pushing the paperwork gently towards him.

'But Delhi would be good experience for me.'

'Jodhpur would be better experience,' I remind him. 'The driving lessons.'

'Next week I make booking,' he promises. 'I planned already to fix this, but small brother, he was sick. I took him from village to city doctor.'

'Couldn't your elder brother have done that? He's nothing more important to fill his day!'

'He can't ride motorbike,' says Mohamd, uncomplaining.

We go to the car to find Sheikh sitting alone, writing his tour report for Mahtani, his yawn telling me he didn't expect to be so late. When Opie ambles out from the shadows, I remind him about the whisky. He grins in anticipation and we wait up well past the time that he'd need for the round trip, before concluding that he must have changed his mind.

Opie stayed in Bhuj – the safari lodge falling short of even his unexacting standards – and, like Sheikh and the boys, he looks better rested than we are.

Sheikh has not yet made contact with Mahtani, but he promises to devote his day to this. He need hardly have come this morning, yet I am pleased that he used the time generously, giving career advice to the boys. He thinks there may be a chance for them to sit the guiding examinations later in the year. He knows some of the people and can make enquiries, even put a good word in the right ear. However, he warns them not to be under any illusions. It's hard work, with no quick routes to easy money. He tells us how, when he was their age, his father suddenly died and it was immediately down to him to support his mother and younger siblings, so he invented a career for himself; starting from zero, he turned himself into one of the most sought-after guides in Udaipur. As he waves us off, I feel an unexpected surge of affection.

I'm not sure what I was expecting from the tribal villages, but for the boys, for Mohamd in particular, they must be embarrassingly close to home. They both manage brave faces of lively interest, but they could scarcely have chosen a worse day to join us and I soon suggest a change of plan: a diversion to the Bhuj City Palace, where immediately they are back in their element, instinctively slipping into guiding gear, using all the knowledge that they can scrape together to animate the displays. Sometimes, Andrew and I know more than they do, having seen more of India. For them, everything is refracted through the single, defining perspective of Jaisalmer, evaluated in terms of its similarities or dissimilarities to that one world.

'We've booked a place for dinner,' says Gajendra at the end of the afternoon. 'At the Prince Hotel. The restaurant's called the Jaisal, so it must be good!'

The pre-dinner starting of Opie's engine is like the bursting of a dike. A torrent of pent-up Opieness gushes forth to show Andrew what he's been missing. Opie talks as if he might never talk again, as if his life depended on it. And he covers an impressive agenda:

*1. A comprehensive enumeration of his virtues qua driver, e.g.
(a) his encyclopaedic knowledge of every conceivable
destination; and (b) his unrivalled driving skills on whatever
terrain has to be crossed to reach the same, rendering jeeps
and, most especially, jeep drivers unnecessary;*

*2. An extensive comparison of these virtues with the well-
known shortcomings of other drivers, e.g. his unique and
profound indifference to commission payments, contrasted with
the notorious rapacity of the competition;*

*3. An exhaustive inventory of the countless ways in which he
alone provides 'added value', e.g. the coveted invitations chez
Madame Opie.*

It's good to see him in such excellent spirits. However, so
blissfully carried away is he with this unsparingly frank self-
assessment that he forgets to keep his foot on the accelerator.
The boys are waiting patiently with some Prince Hotel finger
chips.

'This table is fine?' asks Mohamd, jumping up to greet us. He
has changed for the occasion, sporting a well pressed white shirt.
Gajendra, leaping equally smartly to his feet, looks his consciously
western best in a Tommy Hilfiger tee-shirt.

'You really have to leave?' I ask, thinking how much remains to
be talked about.

'Goppu has one VIP guest on Monday and tonight the bus
goes only to Ahmedabad. Tomorrow night, we take different bus
to Jaisalmer – if all goes well, we reach city by Sunday night. But
you said you go back to Udaipur, no? Maybe I meet you there. It
would be good experience, I think.'

'You mustn't neglect your work. Or your driving lessons.'

'Or the visa application,' adds Andrew.

'But you still haven't told them your news,' prompts Gajendra.

'It's nothing,' mumbles Mohamd.

'He's no longer single!' chuckles Gajendra.

'I'm only engaged,' Mohamd corrects him. 'Also my brothers. To three girls from nearby village.'

'But doesn't that change everything?' I try not to sound dismayed. 'Didn't you think there was more time.'

'Still two, three years, I think. The girl's still young. I haven't seen her, but my father say only fifteen. In any case, my elder brother has to marry first and that won't happen till he has a job. I'm sure I still have time.'

'Mumda has to marry this girl,' says Gajendra emphatically. 'He shouldn't be talking this way. He knows he must respect his parents' wishes. But hey…' He changes the subject to something apparently comic. 'He hasn't told you about Opie.'

Reluctantly, Mohamd recounts an exchange at the safari lodge. Opie buttonholed him near the gate, demanding his share of the commission on my Jaisalmer carpet. 'I told him, "I get no commission from that shop. I explain this before. How can I give you one third of nothing?" He says to me, "You're lying," and I say, "We go to temple and I swear on the God." But what else to do? Only put my hand in my own pocket.'

Gajendra continues chuckling at the absurdity of Opie's behaviour, but now I understand why Mohamd seemed so ill at ease; and why Sheikh stayed until the boys returned to Bhuj; indeed, why he came with them this morning. Anyway, that's the last time they need ever see Opie.

Unless, of course, Mohamd does come to Udaipur.

Deliberately changing the subject, I ask them how the Desert Festival went.

'One Spanish couple, two domestic,' says Mohamd. 'Not much shopping. Not like Goppu. Three rich London couples, who almost empty Riyaz's shop!' With no trace of rancour, he reiterates for Andrew the typical pecking order at the travel agency.

'It could be worse,' chuckles Andrew. 'You could be Muslim, like Mr Sheikh.'

'Hey, maybe travel agent think you *are* Muslim,' laughs Gajendra.

'Muslim name, Hindu boy,' I remind him how he first introduced himself.

'Why do you think your parents did choose a Muslim name?' asks Andrew.

'Also for my brothers,' says Mohamd.

'And your sisters?'

'No. You see, first my parents they have three daughters, but like every Indian family they want sons. So one day, my father visit holy man who is Muslim…'

'Why a Muslim?'

'He just lived near our village. He didn't go to Pakistan with everyone else. But he was wise, according to peoples. So when my father go to see him, asking what must he do to have son, the holy man say, "make promise to give every son Muslim name and you have three". So he promise and he have. Every year, on special day, we pay respect at Muslim shrine. Me and my brothers. Behind my father.'

He frowns, as if his father has cast his shadow once again, while Andrew and I fall silent, taking stock of the many complications in our friend's life. Then Gajendra's ebullience comes to all our rescues. In no time, he jollies us into a mood of hilarity. Even Mohamd turns impishly funny, his serious, shy restraint cast aside. Laughter breeds laughter, as if we're all drunk with each other's company. All the barriers are briefly down. All the usual boundaries separating young and old, rich and poor, insider and outsider. For just a few minutes, we could be any four best pals, out on any town in the world.

An English couple at a neighbouring table has been watching

with a mixture of curiosity and envy. 'Would you like a photo?' asks the wife. She has spotted Gajendra's camera and sensed intuitively that this was a moment to be preserved.

We wanted the meal to make amends for last night's fiasco. We certainly never wanted the boys to think it was 'their turn', but Gajendra is even more insistent than Mohamd, positively wrestling me for the bill. Faced with a choice between saving their pride and saving them an expense which they can ill afford, I settle for the former. Then suddenly they are in a hurry. They have only half an hour to collect their bags and get to the bus station.

We say our goodbyes in the street, standing awkwardly apart. I am wondering how best to do the moment justice, when Mohamd solves my dilemma, translating my self-conscious handshake into a heartfelt hug. 'Till Udaipur,' he calls, as they vanish into the darkness.

There is no sign of Opie. He said he'd wait in the car park but, if he were anywhere there in the shadows, surely he'd have seen us. We try to look conspicuous in the pool of light at the entrance, listening all the time for the start of an engine, but nothing stirs. As our eyes become accustomed to the gloom, we make out six white ambassadors, all driverless. On one of the dashboards, the silhouette of a plastic Ganesh, but no trace of Opie. A kitchen door swings open, illuminating a further parking lot, but the only vehicle there is a minibus. Yet there are figures inside. They may have seen Opie. They may even speak English.

As we start in that direction, the lights suddenly go out and the minibus doors burst open. Two men jump out, running towards us. We look around, calculating the distance back to the hotel entrance, if we made a dash for it. Then we notice that the taller man is pulling on his shoes, while the smaller dons a cloth cap.

'Sorry, sir. Passing time with other driver,' says the husky voice of Sheikh.

'Not thinking finish so early,' adds that of Opie.

'But everything arranged,' Sheikh announces. 'Car to Rajkot, hotel in Bombay, hundred per cent as per your wishes. But with early start, sir, better you move here to Hotel Prince tomorrow night. Maximum persons are preferring. And Mahtani say no extra charge.'

'If only we could move there tonight!' is the prevailing sentiment, as we return to Mike's record-breaking, back-breaking beds.

I have no idea of the village's name. It probably has no name. We only stopped to seek directions. The people live in wigwams, made of branches torn from desert bushes, tangled up with straw, and in every case close to collapse. They suffered badly in the last monsoon, as did their tiny patches of farmland. They have very little to live on. One of the women carries a baby that has fallen on a fire. Its shoulder will not heal. It is raw and oozing puss and there's no money for medical treatment.

'Will she let me pay?' I ask.

'Give one hundred rupees, if you like, but no more,' says Sheikh.

'Surely that can't be enough…' Sheikh's notions of appropriate generosity have always seemed so much greater than my own. He peels off bank notes where I might rummage for change, tipping just about everyone who has anything to do with us, from a man who checks an entry ticket to a farmer whose camels happen to stray in front of my camera.

'Maximum one hundred rupees,' he insists and I do as he says; but even this sparks a flurry of appeals from other mothers. Their own needs are no less great, they clamour, dragging sickly children from all directions. Bony fingers poke me from every side, demanding my acknowledgement of some new wretchedness.

'You've broken the rules again,' whispers Andrew. 'You've singled someone out.' But long after we leave them, I'm tormented by doubt. Could I have helped them all? Should I have tried? Ought we, even now, to turn back? After so many careless, uncounted handouts to people who are mostly undeserving, it seems obscene to start calculating in the face of real misery. Yet I sense the problem from which Sheikh is trying to shield me. There will always be another family, another village.

A little later, we reach the grisly scene of a traffic accident. An Ambassador bearing an elderly Indian couple has collided with a bus. The driver of the car appears to have passed through his windscreen. There is blood on the dust at the side of the road. 'Shouldn't we stop?' I ask, as Opie starts to accelerate. 'Offer to help?'

'Sir, this is India,' says Sheikh. 'If we stopped, we might still be here tomorrow. We can only pray that the police arrive soon.'

'They need an ambulance more than the police.'

'They need the police first, sir. No medical treatment is allowed till the police have all they need.'

'Do we pass a police station?'

'Not on this road,' answers Sheikh, in a way that says, 'Not if Mr Andrew wants to get to Rajkot.'

He takes us to a more prosperous village. There is a general air of festivity and, in one of the larger courtyards, a communal meal is being prepared. A rich lady has died, leaving money for a feast for the whole community but naturally no village party could be so straightforwardly all-embracing. A series of lunches has been held on different days, with invitations working systematically down the social ladder, and today is the turn of the untouchables. I wish I could know how the menus compared.

Several villages later, Sheikh makes an unexpected announcement: 'I think we should see the sea.'

'Fantastic!' cries Andrew. 'We could swim!' Then he remembers how late it is and how far back to Bhuj, with a departure in the small hours, not to mention the farewell dinner that Sheikh has proposed. However, our guide is not to be so easily dissuaded. He's determined to see the sea before returning to land-locked Rajasthan and, unfortunately, between us and the sea there lies the sand.

It all happened so quickly. We were driving down a track beside some dunes, when suddenly Sheikh signalled left towards the sea and immediately, before anyone could question the manoeuvre, Opie spun the car sharply, driving furiously down a sandy slope towards the beach, where we sink into the sand in the depressing way that I remember all too well. Opie starts ripping up bushes to put branches under tyres – a technique that has already proved itself ineffectual – while Sheikh sets off towards a distant, ruined palace, hoping for some form of human presence.

For once, all my sympathies are with Opie. It was Sheikh who insisted that we came here and it was he who told Opie to leave the track... Leaving us how many hours before Andrew needs to leave? Maybe ten?

'We might as well swim,' says Andrew, heading angrily for the beach.

'We haven't time,' I answer tensely.

'It's me who ought to be worried,' he snaps and we paddle along the shoreline without speaking.

'So, what comes next?' Andrew suddenly breaks the silence. 'You still haven't talked about your future.'

He's right. There's been too much in the way. Too much sightseeing. Too much Sheikh. Even too much Mohamd.

'I'm really trying to keep an open mind,' I tell him. 'But actually there's one idea I'm toying with...' Diffidently, I start to outline the palace book idea and find him cautiously supportive.

Indeed, the fact that he doesn't spot some major impediment allows it to start bedding down. However, I'm guiltily conscious of another neglected topic: we haven't talked about *our* future.

'I've missed you,' says Andrew, obliquely re-enforcing the point.

'I've missed you too,' I answer, then properly consider the truth of this. 'It might not always look like that. I haven't been very good at keeping in touch...'

'You've had a lot of distractions,' says Andrew, sounding half sympathetic, half envious.

'And a lot to think through. But I'm getting there,' I tell him. 'India's working. It's doing me good. There's still a way to go, but I've realised this week...' I put an arm round his shoulder. 'I'm beginning to look forward to coming back.'

Andrew smiles gratefully. He knows this is the closest he'll get to reassurance tonight.

The light is starting to fade and we've no idea where in the long line of dunes Opie's car might be hidden. A call produces no response and I do the mental arithmetic: nine and a half hours before Andrew's taxi. Surely Sheikh should have reached the palace... assuming he hasn't found a *chai* shop... or a Mosque for some urgent prayers... Then suddenly, triumphantly, from far along the beach, a horn hoots. Opie has succeeded unaided and we run down the sands to find him revving impatiently. 'You seen guide?' he asks, as if tempted to abandon him.

We find Sheikh on the point of leaving the palace with an unpromising band of conscripts. Far from being delighted by Opie's success, he looks irritated that his own efforts have been rendered superfluous and, as he decommissions his helpers with a round of tips, even this sparks a terse exchange with Opie. Maybe Sheikh was asking for a contribution!

Relations remain edgy throughout the long return drive. I

can't really tell whether Sheikh is annoyed with himself or with Opie. Presumably each is blaming the other. The atmosphere grows even more strained, as we reach the city's outskirts. I thought they both knew their way, but tonight we get badly lost on a variety of ring roads and the mood on the front seat turns positively murderous. It's an unpromising prelude to our dinner.

'Could be a sticky evening,' I whisper to Andrew, as our guide orders for all of us, but I needn't have worried. Sheikh is about to give us plenty to talk about.

He spends a few moments looking uncomfortable, then drops his bombshell: 'I don't know whether to say this. I don't want to spoil the trip, but maybe you notice, there were some tensions between me and the driver?... I don't know why he did that thing. I point to the sea and, next thing, he drives towards it, into the sand. Same thing tonight. He knows the way into Bhuj, but he takes all these crazy turns. I think to myself, if I say something, he'll do more things. So I keep myself quiet. For the sake of the trip... Maximum times, if there are problems between the driver and the guide, we must sort out between us. Not to worry the client. Hundred per cent not to spoil the trip. But, this time, there is some problem with the Opie... This time, I think, I must tell you.'

I have no idea what this can be leading up to, but I am certainly not expecting the tale that Sheikh has to tell.

Seven

'I don't know what happened in Jaisalmer,' says Sheikh. 'I don't want to know. But somehow the driver, he has taken against the Mohammed. Some story about a carpet and he has not given the driver the commission.' This is old news and I am starting to explain, but Sheikh continues: 'Yesterday night, when you came for the dinner, when you were saying goodbye to the boys, the driver had made a plan…' Sheikh hesitates, looking distinctly uncomfortable, then decides to press on. 'Opie had talked with some Delhi drivers. He would point the boys out to them. Then, while he was taking you back to safari lodge, these other men would…' He pauses again, fiddling nervously with his cutlery; then almost inaudibly: 'Teach the boys a lesson.'

For a moment, there is silence. I'm too shocked to respond, but Sheikh continues quickly: 'I don't think anything happened. I don't think anything can have. It was morning time I hear him talk to the drivers, so I make sure I come here last night. I tell Opie I must inform Mr Andrew about his taxi and I sit with him in that minibus, so when the boys are leaving, he cannot point them out.'

There is silence again.

'You mean these drivers were going to ambush the boys? They were going to… *beat them up*?' I ask eventually. 'And this was that man's plan?' Sheikh gives an embarrassed nod. 'I can't continue my trip with him.'

'Sir, he was only …'

133

'*I cannot continue my trip with this driver.* The man's a thug.'

'Patrick's right,' butts in Andrew. 'Mahtani must arrange someone else.'

'Sir, we are here in the Gujarat. When we get back to Udaipur, everything is possible. Hundred per cent then we can speak to Mahtani…'

'That's five days away! I want that Yadav taken off the road NOW! I want to see him never work again. Not for Mahtani, nor for anyone else.'

Sheikh looks at me aghast. He is appalled at the unexpected force of the reaction which he has unleashed and terrified that it might now backfire on him. However, something more important has occurred to me.

'Forget my stupid transport,' I snap. 'We don't *even* know that the boys are all right.'

'Sir, they must be all right. The Opie had no chance to point them out.'

'We don't *know* that. We don't know anything.'

'He might just have given his gangsters a description,' adds Andrew, fuelling my anxieties. 'There can't have been many boys of their age leaving the restaurant last night.'

'We don't *even* know if they caught their bus,' I continue more vehemently. 'They might still be here, in a bloody heap down some dark alley. We won't know for days. They couldn't possibly get to Jaisalmer before tomorrow evening. We won't have any news at all until Monday at the earliest.'

'The big worry,' says Andrew thoughtfully, 'is Mahtani sacking Opie.'

'Exactly! I want this Yadav out of his job! I want him off the road for ever…'

'But if he's sacked, won't he want to get his revenge on Mohamd? If he was capable of this much over some pathetic little commission, what might he do, if he lost his livelihood? He might try to get even with *you*…"

'I have to abandon my trip.'

'Sir, you must not think this way…'

'I mean it. I cannot continue with this driver. Yet, if I explain it all to Mahtani, he's bound to kick Opie out. Then Opie will take it out on Mohamd. I can't have that on my conscience. His safety is more important than my little jaunt across India.'

'I'm sorry you have to deal with this on your own,' whispered Andrew, as he crept away at four in the morning, 'but you mustn't be defeated.'

There seemed to be no way out. No solution that left Mohamd safe and me still in India. I had lain awake all night, chasing each of the logical possibilities round the inside of my head. Every imagined scenario ended disastrously: some with disaster for Opie, some with disaster for Mohamd and some with disaster for me. It reminds me of a play that Alan Ayckbourn wrote, with three different variations on the last act. The audience was invited to decide in the second interval whether it wanted version one, two or three. So, how can I make sure that I get version one? Because I do want version one. I do want disaster for Opie. I've never in my life known such anger, never wanted so much to punish someone. And this anger is churning round with my anxiety. If only I didn't have to wait so long to know whether they are safe.

I no longer trust Opie. I no longer feel safe in his company. Is he stupid enough to think I'd never learn of an attack on the boys? Or that I'd fail to draw the obvious inference? If he was reckless enough to risk his job in that way, might he not equally, in fury, take some other risk with me? Yet how can I get rid of him without simply fuelling his desire for vengeance? How can I hope that Mahtani might handle things in a way which would safeguard my friend? Unless I persuade him that I really mean business, that trouble for Mohamd will mean monumental trouble for his company. I just can't decide. The one certainty is that Opie is the only realistic means of returning to Udaipur, which in turn is the first realistic place to change drivers. But that is four days' drive away. The sights that I planned to see on the way now seem pointless. I simply want to get there as quickly as possible, catch the first plane to Delhi, then go home, all the physical and spiritual good that India has done me knocked away in a single night.

I feel nauseous at breakfast, but put this down to anxiety and lack of sleep. Sheikh bids me a breezy good morning and I tell him not to underestimate how upset I am, then climb into the back of the car without speaking to Opie, without even looking at him. He must have noticed. I always greet him. I always ask him how he is. I wonder whether he knows that I know.

I curl up and try to sleep but, as the journey progresses, I feel steadily worse. Then suddenly I know that we have to stop – stop at once. I wrench my door open, swinging my legs round fast enough to be sick, spectacularly sick, outside rather than inside the car. I slump there immobile, half in and half out, with my head between my knees. I have no strength to move, no will to go anywhere, only sinking despair at the thought of where I am. I feel defeated and alone, utterly helpless and passive. Then they start to lift me back into the car. They want to make me comfortable and, as Opie takes his jacket off, I have a sickening vision of what is about to happen. I can do nothing to resist it, merely closing my eyes, wishing Andrew were here to fend him off, wishing Sheikh at least would intervene, but there's no escape: Opie carefully rolls up the foul-smelling jacket to make a pillow, then he gently places it under my head.

I am too weak to repulse the solicitude of the person I hate most in the world; and this single moment feels like the lowest point of my life.

★

It takes an eternity to reach the Zainabad desert camp. I knew it would be primitive – simple mud huts and basic *charpai* beds, Sheikh confessed when I pressed him – so my hopes are not high, as he helps me from the car. I can barely stand, needing support on either side merely to totter to my hut in the quietest corner of the camp. Zombie-like, I'm no more than dimly aware of what is going on around me, still less able to acknowledge all the consideration that everyone is showing. I am desperate to lie down. Lie down anywhere. It needn't be a *charpai*. Even to sit in an upright position is a struggle, but Sheikh and the owner are fussing with a second feather mattress for my bed and extra pillows. Only with these can I escape from the torture of the vertical.

I drift deliriously through the afternoon, having no sense of time. Sheikh and the owner take turns to bring me water and soup and bananas. Later, when I am more than half conscious, Sheikh comes to sit by my bed. He asks me what I had for breakfast, but I know it wasn't this that made me ill. It was Opie. And frail as I am, I can still manage a spasm of fury that he has cheated me of the satisfaction of spending all this time in India without getting sick. 'You'd better keep that man away from me,' I warn Sheikh, with as much aggression as I can muster.

'Sir, try to put it out of your mind,' he urges me. 'Concentrate on getting better.'

'Tell him to start planning his retirement...'

'Try to stop thinking like a lawyer,' Sheikh beseeches me.

'I'm not thinking like a lawyer,' I answer coldly. 'I'm thinking like a person with a heart.'

Nodding thoughtfully, Sheikh lays a comforting hand on my shoulder. For the first time, I think he understands. 'Sir, sometimes

I am also like this,' he confesses tenderly. 'When someone I love might be hurt.'

It's early evening and I've ventured out. I've dragged myself over to the cosy, covered space where supper will be served, quietly dreading the prospect that I may soon have to be sociable; and, sure enough, I'm quickly joined by the man whom I took to be the owner but who is in fact the owner's son, Dhanraj. He organises toast with more soup, then more bananas, and the food begins to revive me. However, I think it is Dhanraj who does most to perk me up. Latching instinctively onto the depth of my feelings for his country, he gently turns my thoughts in a more positive direction. Then he homes in on the big question, the one I've been careful to avoid for all these weeks: *could my future be in India?*

I can only give an interim answer. Part of me would like to spend some significant time here. Other parts have yet to come to terms with the sacrifices this would mean, but I am startled by his intuitive sureness that the question had to be posed. I decide to risk an explanation of the help I hope to give Mohamd, expecting the usual entrenched opposition, but instead he is intensely supportive. He presses me not to hesitate to bring him to England, telling me how much his country needs people like me. But his passion only fills me with self-doubt. How much of myself am I willing to give?

Soon Sheikh comes to report that he has taken my driver to the village for a talk. All day long, it seems, Opie has been pestering to know, 'What is wrong with the sir?' Finally, Sheikh has had to face the crucial, but ever so slightly awkward conversation where he explains that the beans have been spilled. Oh, and by the way, it was he who did the spilling. But he appears to have survived this ticklish moment unscathed and says that Opie has been asking ever since to come and apologise. Sheikh, thank goodness, told him to leave me alone, until I am well again, which has the happy side effect of leaving him sweating for a day or so, while I decide what to do.

Opie is profoundly worried about his job, believing that I enjoy some special relationship with Mahtani. (Well, long may he continue to think so!) He has promised Sheikh that he'll never again try to hurt the boys. He has also solemnly sworn that they came to no harm on Friday night. Yet how can I possibly trust him? Nothing he says will reassure me, until Mohamd tells me so himself.

Sheikh tries to help me understand. He tells me how worried Opie was about his wife. He explains how little these drivers have to do on the road, except get drunk on cheap whisky; how little they have to talk about, except the commissions they earn – or fail to earn. And Opie did, it seems, miss out on the substantial commission on my Agra table, the makers taking the hard line that the Orchha hotel – not Opie – had introduced me.

Well, maybe... But understanding his point of view does nothing to make it defensible. What he did, or perhaps merely tried to do, still seems unbelievably wicked.

I am still very weak but Dhanraj presses me to make an early morning jeep ride. The jolting discomfort is the last thing I need, but he is quietly insistent. 'There's something you really have to see before you leave,' he urges. 'Trust me.'

We drive out across a vast, barren plateau, the so-called Little Rann of Kutch, stretching out towards the distant, invisible coast, and it is difficult to believe that, when the monsoon comes, this huge tract of land will be flooded by up to two metres of seawater. Today, the salty, baked earth is home to the beautiful Asiatic wild ass, an endangered species, and the last surviving two thousand of them are cantering freely through the scrubby vegetation. Yet, in the wet season, they will all be driven back to the higher ground inland and I imagine them all marooned there, huddled together on some small, dry hillock, waiting for the rain to stop.

'Wonderful, aren't they?' says Dhanraj. 'But they're not why we came.'

As we drive on across the plateau, he tells me how his father used to rule a tiny independent state: just twenty-one villages. And even today, he explains, the family still has a sense of responsibility for its former subjects, putting a fifth of their profits into community projects; once a year, they make the camp available to British schoolchildren, who come to help with building schools and digging wells. Indeed, we pass one of the schools with a painted mural bearing eloquent testimony to the joy of that adventure, but Dhanraj warns me not to underestimate its toughness. They screen huge numbers of applicants to identify those best equipped for the challenge and I know I should probably fail at the first hurdle. Yet I envy what those children found here.

Finally, we come to a halt beside a small, makeshift shelter, standing all alone on a particularly desolate tract of the Rann. Some children are playing, while their mothers bend double in some shallow, rectangular pools, stretching out to one side. These are salt-workers, Dhanraj tells me and his tone leaves me little doubt that this is why we came.

Every year, he explains, as soon as the water recedes and the plain is laid bare, the salt-workers arrive to start a new season's labours. They begin by making the pools. Next they dig twenty-foot wells, from which they pump up the salty, subterranean water to fill the pools. Then they wait patiently in the scorching summer heat, while the water evaporates, until only the salt remains. This they must shovel into sacks, but now they are working fast against the clock. They must finish before the rains return, before everything is washed away again. Everything that they have struggled to build will be destroyed: their pools, their wells, even the little homes that they have made for themselves. Like the wild ass, they must run for the safety of the higher ground.

They have no possessions, no other skills. The owner of the land supplies every piece of equipment and he pays them for what they produce. But he pays them one thousandth of the wholesale price for every sack of salt. A family of six or seven lives on eight thousand rupees a year, about £115 which, even by Mohamd's standards, is breathtakingly little. The children never go to school. None has the smallest hope of any other life. Above all, they must never fall out with the landlord. They have nowhere else to go. No other means of supporting themselves. They are effectively slaves.

Yet the family that we have come to see is clean, brightly dressed and cheerful. The women greet Dhanraj warmly. The children wave at me shyly. There is a boy of about four with a sad, serious beauty, his black hair shining in the sunlight. I long to take him away with me, to give him a chance. As we drive back to the camp, the wind in the jeep blows away my tears.

I have written Opie a letter – bizarrely, I admit, when I am sitting only two feet behind him, but I don't have the strength yet to talk to him and, with no means of knowing what gloss Sheikh might have put on events, I had to make sure that he understood. I am, of course, still dependent on Sheikh for translation services, but it seemed to me the only way that I could clarify why I've been so upset.

The letter tries to explain Mohamd's position and Opie's misunderstanding of it. It also seeks to spell out why he must ensure that Mohamd comes to no harm. Unless he has already come to harm. I still don't know. I tried to call him this morning, in the first of the towns that we drove through, but the lines were down.

What the letter doesn't say is what I am going to do about Opie. I still don't know that either. My determination to see him ruined has been the fiercest negative emotion I've ever felt, the fiercest I ever want to feel. If I do let him off, it will be my greatest act of forgiveness, but I'm not yet well enough to decide. I need to buy time.

We stop again in the next main town and Sheikh helps me over to another Private Call Office, but there is still no Jaisalmer connection. I do, however, have another call to make.

When Andrew left Bhuj he was determined to telephone Mahtani's London associate, as soon as he reached his office this morning. He thought the London man would be more receptive than Mahtani himself to the subtleties of securing Opie's dismissal without the concomitant repercussions for Mohamd. He may be right. This may indeed be what we should do, but I'm still too weak to think clearly. I need a breathing space. And it must already be eight-thirty in London. Andrew should already be at his desk.

Sheikh watches anxiously, as I dial. He knows I'm calling Andrew, but he doesn't know why. The line is quickly answered, but only by his voicemail, which is odd. He said he'd go straight from the airport to his office, but perhaps he's been delayed. I leave a message, asking him not to make the call. Not just yet. I'll explain when we speak... Sheikh, standing at my elbow, is visibly relieved. Opie has at least been given a stay of execution.

Later, we stop for refreshment in a roadside café. Our threesome gathers awkwardly round a single table. I slump there silent and lifeless, propping my head on one hand, while Opie perches bolt upright on the edge of his seat, like a nervous schoolboy, his hands in his lap, hardly daring to move a muscle, yet every so often glancing optimistically towards another PCO, silently willing me to try again. I've not spoken a word to him since Saturday night, nor he to me; but ever since Sheikh filled him in on the purpose of my attempted calls, he has been hankering to stop at every opportunity.

This time the line is working, but some sleepy-sounding cousin of Riyaz, speaking very little English, says neither Riyaz nor Mohamd is there. Yes, Mohamd *is* back in Jaisalmer; but, no, he is not at the shop. I must ring back later, speak to Riyaz, who'll explain everything.

Why do I have to speak to Riyaz? I ask myself, as I put the phone down. And what is there to explain? Is there some news that only Riyaz can be trusted to break to me? Surely, if Mohamd is back in Jaisalmer, he must be OK. Surely the cousin would have said, if there were any problem. Or would he? He didn't have the vocabulary to explain anything complicated. Mohamd could be at the hospital for all I know. *Why ever didn't I ask?*

'You remember that breakfast time in Bhuj?' asks Sheikh, spooning me plain boiled rice.

The Balaram hotel is another converted palace, but more sophisticated than most, almost a health spa, and its comforts are exactly what I was craving yesterday. Yet, if the accidents of geography had brought me here, instead of Zainabad, I doubt it would have done a tenth as much for my recovery.

I still feel the same overwhelming lack of energy, strength and appetite, but confused and incoherent as I am, I know that something has changed. Something at Zainabad has made me see things differently. It has nothing to do with time (even this short span of time) *healing*. This anger had the kind of fire that fuels itself on its own bitterness. It doesn't fizzle out with the simple passage of hours. The shift of perspective owes something to Sheikh's kindness; even more to the generosity of spirit that I saw in Dhanraj; and something beyond rationalisation to my encounter with the salt-workers.

I'm sure Dhanraj knew how much they would affect me. That's why he pressed me to go with him. He knew they would change me. But I'm still too weak and muddled to know what I should really make of the experience. It's true that charity work has always featured on my checklist of possible reincarnations, but always something administrative, something cushioned by the comfortable security of a London desk. Is it remotely possible that I could engage more directly? Or would that be to misread my limitations too disastrously? I'm in no state to say.

'You remember, sir?...' Sheikh can see that I haven't been concentrating. 'That time when we sat with the boys and talked about their problems? I saw myself then. In the Mohammed. Twenty-five years ago. My father just dead and me, starting from nowhere, struggling to make a life for myself.' He pauses, too moved to continue for a moment, and for the first time I feel genuinely close to him. The petty irritations that dogged our days in Gujarat have melted away. 'I have to go to Jaisalmer soon,' he continues. 'I'll see what I can do to help them. But I'll also make some enquiries about the Mohammed and his family. I want to know that the boy is worthwhile. Not like maximum boys in Jaisalmer. I know that you love him as per a son, sir, your own son. I don't want to see your bigheartedness misdirected.' A twinge of irritation: *I wish he'd stick to guiding and leave private investigation to others.* 'But have you spoken to the boy?' He sounds sincerely concerned.

'Not yet. He's not at the shop. He's somewhere in Jaisalmer, but I don't know where he is. Or *how* he is! I'm worried that there's something they're trying to shield me from.'

Sheikh smiles sympathetically, not knowing how to reassure me. After a tactful pause, he addresses his other concern: 'Have you spoken to Mr Andrew?'

'Yes, he had an eight-hour delay at Rajkot. Only just caught the London flight. Didn't even make it to the Bombay hotel!'

'But did he get your message?'

'Oh, yes. He's agreed not to make the call. Not for a day or so. Though he still thinks we should. It's funny – he's normally the forgiving one.'

'Sir, always I am hoping you give the driver the other chance.'

'Simply forget it all? Just hush everything up?'

'Oh no, sir. Hundred per cent I make the full report to Delhi. But still I hope to spare his family from ruin. Not several generations punished for one moment of foolishness.' Sheikh seems so much older and wiser than me, yet I discovered last night, we are almost the same age. 'For the Opie, sir, this was the biggest lesson of his life. He's determined to change his ways, less of the drinking, more of the keeping the client happy, not thinking always about the commission.'

I blame myself. I should never have been so frank about my shopping. Yet the more I think about it, the less I believe this was ever the real problem. The truth lies somewhere deeper, somewhere in what I was trying to do for Mohamd. If only I could think more clearly. It's not that Opie was jealous of the financial support. He didn't even know about it. No, it was surely my attempt to break the mould, buck the system, cross the uncrossable divide. There I was being chauffeured around like some relic of the Raj. Well, that was fine, of course, part of the natural order of things. Until I did the unthinkable: inviting some lowly person from the wilderness to share my superior status, share my car, share the privileged back seat; treating this common desert brat as my equal. And humiliating Omprakash Yadav in the process.

I still haven't addressed a single word to Opie. This isn't a posture. I simply feel physically incapable. For most of my time, I don't even talk to Sheikh. I just curl up as best I can on the back seat, wondering when I shall ever lose this hunger for sleep.

Yet I am dimly aware that the landscape today seems different. It is dotted with huddles of men, sitting in fields on the outskirts of their villages, listening to speeches which, Sheikh explains, are drumming up votes for next week's parliamentary elections. I remember now: the hotels have been blaming a quiet season on the threat of violence at the polls. Well, I hope they are wrong. I've no need of additional drama.

I choose a room in the remotest corner of Poshina's rambling palace. I tell Sheikh that I don't want to see anyone or do anything, but the owner's son is undeterred. He comes to coax me into a walk to a nearby village. 'Tribal people,' he explains, as a friendly family welcomes me to three bare rooms, built from mud and straw, reminding me a little of Mohamd's home in the desert. 'You know about the "scheduled tribes"?'

'Like the scheduled castes?' I ask. 'The untouchables?'

'Technically, they're completely separate from the caste system. They're India's aborigines. In this village, they belong to the Bhil tribe. Farmers, like they've been for centuries. But yes, they're much like the scheduled castes in terms of status – not to mention job allocations and reserved seats in Parliament.'

Life in the Bhil community seems one of gentle, harmonious monotony, wholly given over to the growing, grinding, cooking and eating of millet. Well, that and the drinking of some lethal home brew – no doubt millet-based – which, to judge from the general unsteadiness, the male population has been imbibing assiduously. Suddenly and for no obvious reason, they take it into their heads to give me an archery display.

'Is this for hunting?' I flinch as one of the more sober participants shoots an arrow uncomfortably close. 'Or just a hobby?'

'It's neither,' laughs my hotelier. 'It's for killing people from other villages. There are seven or eight revenge killings every year. And this is the tribe from which the region's MP will be elected!'

BEFORE

★

I've spoken to Mohamd and he's fine. They got away from Bhuj unharmed. Yet not without incident. When they returned to their guesthouse for their bags, there was a message. Two men – drivers from Delhi, the hotelkeeper thought – had invited them to meet in a nearby café and, innocently imagining one of these to be our driver, they saw no reason not to go. However, finding no Opie, they simply continued on their way to the bus stand.

Does this mean the men were there in the cafe, but unable to recognise the boys, because they hadn't been identified? Or had the drivers decided it was pointless keeping the rendezvous, with their victims unknown? It hardly matters. Either way, it proves that Opie was planning something.

Mohamd sounded perfectly relaxed; but of course, he'd try to sound relaxed, even if he were petrified. I tell him to be watchful, not to go to any more mysterious meetings. However, I promise him that Opie is under no illusions. He knows that if Mohamd comes to any kind of harm, he'll never work again.

But he may never do so anyway. I've still not decided.

Eight

I was expecting Mount Abu to be icy. According to Sheikh, it was the third highest point in the country but, visiting the famous Jain temples, I was actually glad of the shade. Indeed, I even managed a swim. Yes, a swim... You see, things have changed. I've spoken to Opie.

The day started badly. My supposedly peaceful room turned out to be cruelly close to the mosque and its amplified six-thirty call to prayer. I was therefore in no mood to be chatty, when we stopped at the Rajasthan border to pay our road tax. Yet it was here, in a roadside café, that I decided the time had come.

'Opie, I think we need to talk.'

'Yessir.' He looked at the table.

'Mr Sheikh has read you my letter? Told you in Hindi what it says?'

'Yessir.' He stared more fixedly at the table.

'You understand why I was upset? Why it made me ill?'

'Yessir... Sorrysir.' Opie looked about to disappear *under* the table.

'At first I was angry. I wanted to punish you. I've never so much wanted to punish anyone in my life. I wanted to make sure you never worked again. But in our religion, we believe it's important to forgive.' I was simplifying my theology at this point and hesitated for a moment over the 'we'. I wasn't sure what I believed. But I did know with absolute certainty that it was important – *important to me* – to try to forgive him. 'If I do,' I emphasised, 'it will be one of the most difficult things that I've ever done. Do you understand?'

'Yessir.' He looked at me for the first time.

'So you must do something that will be difficult for you. You must write to Mohamd and apologise. You must promise that you'll never try to harm him. Then you must show the letter to Mr Sheikh, so he can tell me what you've said.'

'Yessir.'

'Will you do that?'

'Yessir... Thankyousir.'

He was greatly relieved. So was Sheikh. And so in fact was I. I feel transformed, as if blood has returned to veins from which the circulation has too long been cut off.

Opie has driven me to a restaurant for my first proper meal since Bhuj, but the no-choice, no-nonsense menu is served at such velocity that I am finished and back in the street within twenty minutes. Opie thinks this immensely funny and it's the first time we've laughed together for a long while. He starts a torrent of explanations and excuses, but I cut him short. I am too tired. He must just write his letter. Then it will all be finished.

'How many nights?' asked Opie, when Sheikh had been dropped at his Udaipur office. It felt like old times. Except that, on this occasion, I hadn't really thought about it. All I knew was, I wanted to stop in one place, for as long as possible. I was tired of living out of suitcases, tired of no longer even remembering what was in them... not to mention simply tired. It would be a waste of an expensive car and driver, but all I could think of was the relief of unpacking in a familiar room, where everything already had its place.

'Five nights,' I answered on the spur of the moment, watching his face fall.

'You make any small excursion?'

'Maybe the Monsoon Palace,' I offered as a half-consolation. 'I can call you at the office... But remember you've a letter to write!'

Room 31 is hardly out-sized, yet I am basking in the pleasure of *space*: no more Sheikh, no more Opie, neither of them nudging at the corners of my day. I hang up a 'do not disturb' sign and stretch on the bed, conscious of nothing but the laundry slapping on the lakeshore and the children playing cricket in the alley. Then I remember Mohamd. He said he might try to meet me here. My solitude may be about to be shared. But how could he hope to come so soon? He only reached Jaisalmer four days ago. Surely just something he said to sound willing. Yet he did make it to Gujarat, against all expectations.

I drift off to sleep, dreaming that I am driving into Opie's village for my farewell dinner. Mohamd, Gajendra and Riyaz are all squashed in the front next to Opie, while Sheikh and Mahtani cling together on the roof, like passengers on the top of an Indian bus. The space beside me on the back seat is empty, save for a pile of first editions of my newly published book on the Palace Hotels, which I have just finished signing. Mrs Opie, looking much like the fearful goddess Kali, comes out to meet me, bearing a single flute of champagne on a silver salver. The house behind her resembles the Brighton Pavilion, only more imposing. Down a white marble staircase run two small children, bearing plates of poppadoms, topped with caviar, which they promptly drop and the crash of the broken china wakes me up.

The clatter is simply the noise of dinner being served in the restaurant over my room. I must have slept for a long time and I'm ravenous. However, before I can deal with the hunger, there is a message pushed beneath the door. It reads like a riddle – *POLICE BUSY ELECTIONS WORK SORRY (M. NAYAK)*. At first, I fail to make sense of it, understanding only from the 'sorry' that he won't be coming. Then I work it out: in the run-up to the elections the police are preoccupied with maintaining order, so even the likes of Mohamd can find employment. I had all but written off the idea of his coming, but now that it's out of the question, the days ahead seem oddly empty.

The upstairs terrace is nearly full, the only free table in a dark, unaccustomed back corner. Like everyone else, I wanted a view of the lake. What I get is the television aerials and air-conditioning machines of the neighbouring buildings. Leaving most of my food, I wander down to one of the nearby washing ghats, now dark, deserted and silent, the teeming commotion of the day just a memory. I stop to rest on the lakeside steps for what seems like an hour or more, wondering how long it will be before my energy comes back.

No 'art students' on this side of the lake, I reflect with a kind of nostalgia. 'But anyway, you don't have the strength,' I chuckle, as I haul myself back to my feet to return to my room. Then suddenly a knife flashes at my elbow and I turn to see a strikingly beautiful boy, barely waist-high. He is barefoot, scruffy and thoroughly grubby from too many hours on the streets; but his face would stop anyone in his tracks. As, of course, would the knife.

His dangerous dark eyes fix on mine, as he flourishes the blade for sale. 'Hundred rupees,' he says, flicking the steel fast and close to encourage me to make up my mind. Is it the knife or the piercing beauty that feels so threatening? A glimmer of interest and I know I shall never shake him off. Reluctantly, I look away, pushing past him to retrace my steps to the safety of the hotel. He tugs at my arm, darts ahead in my path, tries everything to win eye contact. I so much want to look again. I want to understand that beauty, plant it in my memory, but I dare not give it a second glance.

★

The architecture book sits accusingly on the bedside shelf. The City Palace looms reproachfully through the bedroom window. But I've woken late. It must already be hot. I need all of my energy for a walk to The Voice of Trade and Travel.

'He's out of town with important client,' says the nervous-looking youth manning Sheikh's office. Too late, he sees that this sounded tactless. 'VIP,' he stresses, digging himself deeper. 'My name is Dilip,' he volunteers, running an agitated hand through prematurely grey hair. 'I have tension,' he adds, as if to explain the grey. However, he knows about the letter. He has no idea where my driver is, but he is confident that the communication is about to be written.

'Will Mr Sheikh translate it?' I ask.

'Sir, I think for sure he do this. But first your tour… For Monsoon Palace, tomorrow morning at five is OK?'

'Maybe later in the week.'

'Or out to dinner?'

'I'll be fine, Dilip. Now about the letter…'

'Don't worry,' he says, looking worried himself.

Near the hotel gateway, a tailor calls a greeting from a tiny open-fronted booth, like a soldier's sentry box. 'First time in Udaipur?' he asks amiably.

'Third,' I correct him, sounding smug, but the exchange detains me long enough to notice the sign above his head. He undertakes 'alterassions', which is the best news in days. I've lost some weight in the recent weeks – especially the last one – and my trousers and shorts are all too loose.

'Six o'clock,' the tailor promises, accepting the consignment of everything that I'm not currently wearing.

I set off in search of a subject for a painting. There are plenty of candidates. It's just that they seldom coincide with anywhere I can sit without being trampled by wandering cattle. Eventually I set myself up near a lakeside temple. The drawing alone takes several hours and, in the end, the mosquitoes as much as the fading light tell me I must finish it tomorrow.

'How much?' I enquire at the sentry box.

'How much you like,' says the tailor, predictably.

I reckon that a tenth of the going rate in London will be ten times the going rate here and leave it at that. I'd never get it right, if I stayed here all year.

'Sir, you like auto-rickshaw?' says each of four eager drivers at the hotel gate. 'Price very less,' adds the most honest-looking.

'Maybe later.' I indicate the armfuls of tailoring and painting materials.

'No problem. I am waiting.'

'I have to take a shower.'

'Still I am waiting,' he assures me and I resign myself to the inevitable. The moment that I step outside, all four drivers pounce, but I stick with the trustworthy face. 'Shiv Niwas,' I instruct him.

'*Hotel* Shiv Niwas?' he queries in a mixture of amazement and delight.

The Shiv Niwas belongs to the Maharana – the local equivalent of Maharaja – and is, I remember from my dinner there with Andrew, the last word in Udaipur luxury. Its patrons more typically arrive by gleaming Mercedes, ancient Ambassador at the very least, not a dusty, rattling rickshaw, so no wonder the rickshaw man looks delighted. Already imagining the supper that his family can now afford, he scurries to his vehicle, lifting the driver's seat to extract a plastic bottle filled with fuel. Carefully, calculatingly, he pours into the tank what he judges to be sufficient, then thinks for a moment and adds a little more. After all, he now has the shopping to do.

'How much?' I ask, with a sense of *déjà vu*, at the Shiv Niwas gate.

'How much you like,' he replies, glancing hopefully at the opulence of our surroundings, and I peel off a note, which he takes without a flicker of pleasure or its opposite. Instinct tells me it is insufficient, so I proffer another, which is accepted with the same impassive air. Instinct now tells me that even my opening bid was excessive. This is clearly the first thing you learn at rickshaw driving school: the more prodigal the customer, the more deadpan the expression; always leave him with the lingering worry that he might have been stingy.

I am shown to an open-air table beside the white marble swimming pool. A sign says that bathing hours have ended, but an overweight Indian is defiantly demonstrating his pounding backstroke. The well-to-do diners at the surrounding tables are mostly venting their displeasure on the staff, as if hectoring a waiter might counterbalance the unfamiliar sense of subjugation to an ego bigger than their own. Hoping that Andrew and I were never quite so full of our own importance, I can hardly wait to leave.

A few minutes from the Caravanserai, a youth rushes up to me in the shadowy street. 'Hello! Sir? Please!' He beckons me over to a dimly lit shop. 'Here, sir! Come!' The shop is packed with local lads and beaded, bearded westerners in equal numbers and at the front of the queue is another young man, ladling milky white drinks from a large, dark cauldron. 'Hello! Sir? Please! This *bang shop* – you want special *lassi*?' I don't. At least I don't think I do... 'Come, sir, live dangerous,' says the youth, tugging my elbow, and I am half way to the counter, when it occurs to me that Mohamd will probably telephone again.

'I'm glad there's plenty of work,' I tell him, when the call comes through.

'Not today,' he says glumly. 'Young couple, they say, "Too many palaces already. Only we want to sit by swimming pool."'

'Maybe tomorrow?'

'Yes, maybe tomorrow.'

He enquires after my own day and I struggle for something to report. 'I started a painting,' I answer limply.

'You finish tomorrow?' he asks encouragingly.

'Yes, maybe tomorrow.'

We both laugh a little at the unintended echo.

'What about the visa forms?' (Always easier to organise someone else's life than my own.) 'There's not much time, if you want to come in the summer.'

'Next week I go to Delhi,' he promises.

Then I explain about the Opie letter, sensing, even as I do so, how bizarre the notion sounds. 'Will you call me tomorrow?' I persist. 'If the letter comes?'

'Normally the post is not so quick.' He sounds bewildered and promises instead to call me at Neemrana to say goodbye, thus reminding me that the stretch of days, which once seemed so joyously numberless, can now be counted.

Sheikh's office was closed. A pencil message on a piece of cardboard said that someone would be 'back at two o'clock'. Turning to go, I saw a familiar-looking Ambassador, parked in the shade. The windows were open, so I crossed to peer inside, expecting to find Opie snoring happily; but the dashboard had a dancing Shiva where the Ganesh should have been. A hefty muscleman was lumbering towards me, about to defend his vehicle… Until he heard the name of Opie. Then he laughed in the same disconcerting way that Mahtani had done. 'Oh yes, there's only one Opie,' he repeated the catchphrase. But no, he didn't know where he was, still less whether he was up to date with his correspondence.

My return took me past the City Palace. 'Your last chance,' the frown of the lady in the ticket booth seemed to say, but the book was in my room. I was spared. On the other hand, I did have my camera. I was snared after all. But no, there was a painting to finish. Spared again! Then the ticket seller pinned me to the spot with a reproving stare: only the definitive photographic record seemed likely to appease her.

'Two films,' I bragged to the burly stranger sitting next to me at lunch. 'Every possible detail!'

'I am also photographer,' he replied, washing hearty quantities of curry down with large swigs of beer. 'I photograph all His Highness's properties.' In the first sentence, I noted a German accent; in the second, a passionate delight in his subject. 'Robert Huber.' He offered a food-stained hand; then wiped it on his shirtfront, before rummaging in a rucksack for some samples of his work. 'Samode,' he explained, passing a large colour plate.

'You're a professional?' I asked, while my jaw dropped.

'Exactly. And this is Dungarpur.' The palace had never looked so spectacular. 'But this is the important one...' Robert's sunset view of Udaipur was taken from a hilltop. The streetlamps were lit, yet it was still not quite dark. An enchanted pink glow tinted the pale, bluish-white buildings. 'To get it like this, I climbed up three nights in a row,' he reminisced, still guzzling rice.

'It's magnificent,' I told him.

'The Maharana thinks so too. He said to me, "I've never seen my city like this. You must photograph all my palaces, all my birthday celebrations...".'

'You've become the court photographer?'

Robert chuckled, mopping food from his face with the back of his arm. A less likely courtier it was hard to imagine. 'See this. It's a suite in the Shiv Niwas, but no one's ever taken this shot. A huge screen at the entrance blocks the view. Yet if you stand on the other side, you're too close. I said to the flunkeys, "The screen's got to go," and they said, "No one's ever moved it, not in a hundred years". "Ask His Highness," I said and they called his private office. You should have seen their faces... "If Robert says it's got to go, it's got to go," said the Maharana.'

'So they moved it?' I asked, impressed, as Robert downed the last of his beer and heaved himself to his feet.

'Exactly. The artist as revolutionary!' he laughed, lumbering off for a well-earned siesta.

Only then does the penny drop: I've found the perfect collaborator for the book, yet I let him go without even asking him for contact details.

'Sir, call for you!' shouts a waiter, as he beckons me over to the kitchen.

'You've had the letter?' I ask excitedly, above the cooking noises. But no: there was nothing in today's post.

'I called with other news,' says Mohamd. 'My older brother just got married.'

'Already?' I try to take this in. 'Weren't the three of you supposed to be married together? And only after he'd got himself a job?'

'Yes, but everything's changed. It's all gone wrong. He's married a different girl.'

Nine

'My parents don't know,' says Mohamd. 'My brother, he has small place in city – single room, near that place we meet camelman. The girl is there. My brother meet her two months before, at cousin's marriage. I knew he liked her, but never I thought he would do like this.'

'You never thought he'd show such initiative,' I think to myself.

'She is city girl,' he continues. 'From Ajmer.'

'Your brother went all the way to Ajmer?' I marvel at the transforming power of love.

'No,' Mohamd laughs. 'He never travel more than fifty kilometres. For that marriage, the girl come to Jaisalmer. After, they write letters. Finally she leave her family, come again to Jaisalmer, make marriage in secret.'

'Surely your family's bound to find out.'

'Of course. This place where my brother live, it belong to my father. Every month, he stay there when he go to city. But my brother hope he understand – now that marriage is done.'

'You think that's possible?' I ask, remembering the forbidding figure in the army greatcoat.

'Not really. Like I told you, my brother was engaged to that other girl from nearby village.'

'And presumably this new one's the wrong caste.'

'No, she is also Nayak. That part is fine. But she is not the girl from nearby village. My father made a contract.'

'And your brother broke it.'

'I think definitely I must go to Delhi,' says Mohamd.

'Sorry, sir,' said Dilip, when I telephoned. 'Mr Sheikh again outside city.'

'When will he be back?'

'Late, sir, but tonight he invite you to restaurant.'

'I need to know about the letter.'

'Mr Sheikh tell everything tonight, sir.'

I rang off in defeat, calling the Shiv Niwas instead, hoping to get a lead on Robert Huber, but the name meant nothing to the receptionist. 'The man who moved the screen,' I prompted to no avail. I'd have to try my luck at the Maharana's private residence.

'Room number,' demanded a bayonet-bearing guard at the gate, serving both the private quarters and the hotel complex.

'I'm not a hotel guest.' I hesitated – this was the first time I had said it: 'I'm a writer.'

'No journalist,' said the sentinel firmly.

'Not that kind of writer,' I mumbled feebly. If I carried on like this, how could I expect to be taken seriously? 'More of a book writer.' The guard merely sniffed, as if this carried equally low status, then glanced at a list of the day's approved visitors, pursing his lips and shaking his head. 'I'm a colleague of Mr Huber,' I threw in hopefully, as he checked again, finding no one of that name either. 'The German photographer,' I added in desperation and his face lit up.

From the back of the sentry box, came a full length photographic portrait and he pointed excitedly, first at the likeness, then at the genuine article. 'Same, same,' he explained, in case I had missed the similarity, adding awestruck: 'You work with Mr Robert?'

This small stretching of the truth secured a telephone

connection to the Maharana's private office, but a female voice told me briskly, there was no need to enter. Robert had left for Deogarh. And no, he didn't have a mobile telephone. 'Hardly Robert's style!' she laughed. 'Anyway, mobiles never work outside Jaipur.'

Improbably, Robert did have an email address, which is why I spent the rest of the morning in the closest Udaipur gets to an internet café: a friendly bookseller, lending out his own computer for a modest hourly rate. The message to Robert, that I hoped to reach Deogarh in a couple of days, needed only a minute; my report for Andrew on the latest in Mohamd's life scarcely longer. What took the time was the backlog of incoming mail from friends. It fell into three distinct categories: the early messages upbeat, supportive, good-naturedly envious; the second batch grumpier, fed up with the European winter and resentful of my failure to reply; then finally the *not long now* collection, all insistently asking what comes next. I sent them each a standard text, giving a brief account of both my travels and my computer problems, but avoiding the big question.

The afternoon I then wasted. That is to say, I finished my painting of the lakeside temple and immediately tore it up. It was too inhibited: I needed to let go. I decided to work off my frustration back in my room. With the same subject and a fresh sheet of paper, I put down big, bold outlines in confident ink, then washed in bright slashes of watercolour, lifted directly from the paintbox, using fast, exuberant brush strokes. Most importantly, I stopped before it all looked too 'finished'.

It pleases me more than anything to date but, when I show it to Sheikh, he looks bemused, managing something non-committal to the effect that it might make a present for Mr Andrew. Then, quite unexpectedly, he puts a fatherly arm around my shoulder. 'Sir, I am sorry not to spend here more time with you. Not as your guide, but as your friend.' I am not sure how to respond. We have been through a lot together. At times I even felt close to him, yet I can't quite reciprocate this signal of something warmer.

'It's good to have this farewell dinner,' I answer awkwardly. 'As long as there are no more surprises!'

'No, sir,' he laughs. 'Only, because I was outside city, I have not seen the Opie.'

'So, you don't know about the letter?'

'Hundred per cent I shall check, sir. But Dilip say tomorrow you go to Roopangarh. From there you must visit the Pushkar, but remember, sir, for blessing prayers, maximum thirty rupees.' I have no idea what he is talking about, but prayer meetings are low on my agenda.

'I need to know that it's gone,' I insist. 'I need to feel this is finished.'

There is a rumble of thunder as I pay my bill, but the receptionist ignores this: it never rains in the tourist season. Instead, he tells me, Mr Sheikh called to see me, before I was up.

'Did he leave anything?' I ask. 'Any message? Or an envelope?'

'No, sir, just he came to say goodbye.'

'Has he sent it?' I round on Dilip, who has run in to join us, as a flash of lightning illuminates the alley.

'Oh, for sure, sir.' He looks sincere, but is no doubt simply telling me what he thinks I want to hear. It's considered more courteous than the truth. 'Maybe yesterday.'

'Do you know what it said?'

'I think, not really, sir.'

This is hardly what I intended when I did my deal. Nothing in India ever works out quite as you intended. So much slips through your fingers, no matter how tight your grip. I don't even ask about the translation.

The first plops of rain prompt a dash to the car. For a moment, I hardly recognise Opie. He has shaved off his beard and mumbles something to the effect of a new image for a new beginning. The rain swells rapidly to a downpour and the rank of rickshaws looks set to be washed away. I wave goodbye to the tailor in his open-fronted booth, huddled flat against the back wall, nursing someone's sodden trousers. 'Winter monsoon,' laughs Opie, now, without his beard, looking more the clown than the villain, as he ploughs his reckless course through the flooded bazaar.

'Dilip says you've written to Jaisalmer?' I ask, getting swiftly down to business.

'Yessir.'

'And you posted it yesterday?'

'Yessir.'

'And you've said what I told you to say?'

'Yessir.'

Well, he would say that, wouldn't he? Hardly the most searching of cross-examinations! But at least the storm is over. The sun is inching out again.

'This temple by Pushkar Lake, this only Brahma temple in India,' says my new-look driver. 'All are these pilgrims coming, but always only twenty rupees you give...' Give to whom? And for what?' I wonder, but Opie has already started the next chapter of the briefing: 'This Pushkar, many hippies. Not good class of persons.'

Well, he's right about the quantity. I've never seen so many relics of nineteen-sixties hippiedom in one place. On second thoughts, most of them are too young to have been alive in the nineteen-sixties. They just look the same. With perfect integrity, the essentials of the faith have been passed from generation to generation and the bazaar, rising thoughtfully to their needs, sells little but tie dyed garments and incense sticks. I never learn where the real people of Pushkar shop. I never learn whether Pushkar *has* any real people. What it does have is a vast number of beggars, lamenting a wide variety of misfortunes; also swarms of self-styled holy men, whose principal religious observance consists of demanding to be photographed, then demanding to be paid.

The first person (other than the hippies) who neglects to ask for money is a youth, who accosts me in the crowd with a small yellow flower, which he plants in the pocket of my shirt. 'I am Brahmin,' he tells me as if this explained everything. I expect to be charged for the flower, but he seems content merely to run through the usual questionnaire as to my name, nationality and profession. Indeed, so startled am I by this lack of commerciality that I slip into old bad habits. 'I'm a lawyer,' I tell him and he smiles approvingly.

I was not paying much attention to our route, but now I see that we have reached the water's edge, where two Nordic-looking teenage girls are sitting cross-legged beside a white-robed Indian. He has just tied a red string bracelet round each of their left wrists. They are putting their heads together, conferring, and one of the girls is unzipping her money belt, extracting a ten rupee note. This must be one of Sheikh's blessing ceremonies and I am amused to see them undercutting both his and Opie's budget figures.

Before I have even completed this thought process, my young companion has somehow steered me closer. Without intending to, I have taken the place of the girls at the lakeside. Sitting likewise cross-legged, I am holding spices and rose petals in my cupped hands and struggling to repeat a succession of prayers in what I take to be Hindi. Talking faster and faster, the man is leading me in prayers for myself, prayers for my father, prayers for my sister, prayers for my friends... It goes on forever, with my attempted mimicry veering ever more ludicrously wide of the mark. I started off with a certain ecumenical openness to the idea, but my gibberish is making a mockery of one of

Hinduism's most sacred places and I resent the way that this Brahmin's greed has made me his accomplice in undermining that sacredness. Because greed is what this is all about. A 'donation' of three thousand rupees is finally demanded and I flatly refuse anything comparable.

'*What?*' he shrieks, in the well-practised, scandalised tones that are calculated to cause an effective level of discomfiture. 'You come here to holy place? You rich man? You well-paid lawyer?' It is too late now to disabuse him, impossible to explain that I have said goodbye to both the profession and the pay. 'You come here from London. You have most important blessings for yourself, for your family, for your friends? And you think they not worth so much? And you very rich lawyer...'

He has, however, underestimated my embarrassment threshold. My best and final offer is sixty rupees, only two percent of the requested contribution (albeit double the figure advocated by Sheikh, not to mention three times Opie's absolute maximum). Needless to say, this is not a level of munificence that goes down well on the ghats. There is an aggressive chorus of disapproval from fellow Brahmins all along the shoreline.

'How much?' demands Opie, as he spots the red braid on my wrist.

'That's my business,' I answer stiffly.

'Will it all have changed?' I wonder, as we drive through the Deogarh bazaar. Two years ago, when I first came here, the palace had only just started taking guests: a mere six rooms and Western faces still a novelty. Children in the village, knowing nothing of pens, followed us everywhere in tight, undemanding huddles. The youngest, barely able to walk, were led forward by their grandfathers to learn their first handshake. A young tailor, who sewed a button on my shirt, refused payment, but gave me tea.

And there he is now, rushing forward from his pedal-powered

Singer to clasp my hand through the car window! He points delightedly to one of my buttons, then calls to fellow stallholders, excitedly recounting the repair of over a year ago. Then an urgent tapping on the opposite window: could this tousle-haired adolescent be the urchin I photographed, sucking the biggest gob-stopper in the history of sweet-making? He sticks his tongue in his cheek to prove I'm right, then runs off to spread the word.

'I'll walk from here,' I say, leaving Opie to take the bags, and I am instantly mobbed by small children, their greetings as tactile and unacquisitive as before. Many just want to take my hand; others refuse to let me pass until I've joined in their cricket game. Shopkeepers all along the route smile and wave, as they nudge one another in recognition.

There is an even greater sense of home-coming, as I step into the first of the palace's courtyards. Vibhu, the aristocratic owner's eldest son, speeds forward to greet me. He has remembered which room I stayed in, even the samosas that I like to have for lunch. 'Lucky you phoned us,' he says. 'We've done up ten more rooms but, with your booking, we're full.'

'Is Robert Huber staying?' I ask eagerly.

'He left for Jaipur.' Vibhu smiles apologetically. He has lost none of his good looks, the luxuriant length of his hair more Bollywood hero than Rajput ruler. 'We wanted photos of all the rooms but, with all the rooms occupied... He'll be back next month. Can you stay till then?' he jokes.

'Don't remind me!' I groan. 'I've got less than a fortnight.'

'All the same, it's a good long tour you're doing. The law must be profitable.'

'Not any more,' I start to explain. It's a tale that I'm well versed in telling but suddenly, as I tell it this afternoon, I wonder whether anyone believes me. Perhaps they all think I was given the sack – dismissal being so much more plausible than the real explanation – and the more I try to make the story credible, the more spurious it sounds.

My efforts are interrupted by a sprinting waiter with a cordless telephone. It's Mohamd. I gave him the number in a letter sent from Udaipur, but that was his only mail. Nothing from Opie.

'Perhaps tomorrow,' I offer half-heartedly.

'But I won't be here. That's partly why I called. I'm leaving for Delhi, early morning.'

'And your father?' I puncture the mood of optimistic adventure.

'Still he doesn't know. That's why I have to go now. I don't have much time.'

I've been trying to paint the picture that I always planned to paint in Deogarh: the fruit and vegetable market where the women from the countryside bring their crops. I looked hard for somewhere to set up my stool, somewhere not too deep in squashed produce, somewhere safely apart from the unrelenting tide of shoppers. However, I soon had a large audience, perhaps fifty people, crowding in tight concentric circles, hiding my 'subject'. I had to make most of it up but, against all the odds, did my intentions something close to justice – for the first time, even signing the end result. As I walked back through the bazaar, everyone asked to see it. I had become a curiosity.

'Sir, there was a call,' says the receptionist. 'Someone called Nayak. He said he'd ring again in ten minutes, but this was half an hour before.'

'I'll wait here,' I suggest, heading for a courtyard, where chairs have been arranged for an evening entertainment.

'Tribal dancing,' explains the receptionist, as some savage-looking performers arrive. 'Bhil people.'

I take a cautious step backwards. 'The last Bhils I met liked to get drunk and then shoot each other.'

'Not these,' he laughs. 'You remember Udaipur crest outside City Palace? One side Bhil chief, the other Rajput prince, because – four hundred years before – these Bhils, they fight for Maharana.'

The tribesmen have started playing, drawing guests from their rooms. A boy with red and white earrings, like Mohamd used to wear, steps forward to dance: his ankle bracelets, hung with bells, stamp an infectious rhythmic carillon. He somersaults upside down to dance on his hands, but I am called away to the telephone.

'You're in Delhi?' I ask, knowing it has to be Mohamd.

'I'm in Jodhpur,' he confesses.

'But the visa? You were going to the Embassy.'

'My father sick. Small heart attack. Last night I bring him to hospital. Now, I think, he's OK,' he adds, as if I might be worried.

'Couldn't your useless brother have taken him?'

'Like I tell you, only fifty kilometres he has gone.'

'But you said yourself – there wasn't much time.'

'Even less, I think, now. You see, my father knows. He saw that girl, my brother's wife.'

'Hence the heart attack?'

'I think so, yes,' he answers solemnly.

'And the trip to Delhi?'

'When I get back. Maybe two, three days' time.'

'So you're writing a book with Robert?' asks Vibhu's mother bluntly, her simple, pale yellow sari somehow looking dauntingly regal, as she joins me for tea.

The Rani of Deogarh must be the most effortlessly aristocratic person that I've met. Even her daughters-in-law perform a kind of curtsey to touch her feet when they greet her. She has no airs, no intention to impose; she is naturalness itself. Yet I'm still very much in awe of her and hesitate before answering, convinced that she'll think me underqualified.

'It's nothing definite. Robert doesn't even know about it.'

'You should do it,' she insists. 'The boys are very keen.'

As if on queue, her other son, Shatru, rushes up. 'Vibhu's told me all about it. We really need a book like yours. Every room has a history here, but there's never time to tell the guests. You should talk to my father – he's done a lot of work on this.'

I've always felt equally in awe of Rana Nahar Singh. He is in no way physically daunting, being both shorter and thinner than his two strapping sons. He dresses simply and speaks quietly, yet it needs only a moment in his company to sense the incisive intellect and iron principles. He is a major authority on the history of the region's miniature paintings and his sons say he should write a book on them. A jeep excursion with him last time gave Andrew and me a privileged glimpse of the old world of Rajasthani princes: we saw where he shot his first panther; we heard how his last elephant died; and we witnessed the unforced respect which he still inspired throughout the region. Not that he had lived on the ghosts of his power. When Independence came, he embarked on another life, with a different kind of authority – as a history teacher at Ajmer's Mayo College.

The school was founded by the Viceroy in 1875, to educate India's Princes in a manner that would fit them for the British Empire – the pupils in its heyday living the most exclusive of lives, often with retinues of personal servants, even their own mini-palaces. Post-Independence, the Rajput community still made up the core of the intake, both Vibhu and Shatru among them.

Nahar Singh is cautiously helpful, promising to fix me up with some introductions. 'The first thing you must read is *The Annals and Antiquities of Rajasthan*. It's in two big volumes, but you'll find it in Delhi.' He pauses, fixing me with his penetrating, schoolmasterly stare. 'You realise what you'd be taking on, I suppose? It's a demanding project.'

'But I want a demanding project,' I insist, sounding less convincing than I hoped.

Mohamd called at breakfast time. He was still stuck in Jodhpur, hoping his father would be better in a day or so.

'What about the driving school? That was in Jodhpur, wasn't it?'

'I think maybe visa more important…'

'You could still book some lessons.'

'You're right,' he admitted. 'I was little bit lazy. Tomorrow, definitely.'

'Or even today?'

'Today, yes, for sure.'

'But how is your father taking the news? Your brother's marriage, I mean.'

'He says we'll all be ruined. Thrown out from society.'

'Can it really be that bad?'

'I'll know when we get back,' he said sombrely. 'The parents of the other girl, the one my brother engaged to, they don't know yet. Or they didn't when we left. That's why I need to know where you'll be. To keep in touch.'

'You're right.' It's a good thing one of us is being practical. 'It's Jaipur tonight. In the Samode people's Haveli, I hope. Then some tiger-spotting in Ranthambore…'

'This is jungle location. No good telephones. You know which place after?'

'I haven't decided.' This is almost like dealing with Opie. 'Maybe the Samode Palace again.'

'I'll find the number,' he said decisively. 'Definitely by Wednesday I'll call.'

★

The drive to Jaipur meant six hours of dense traffic on the highway. I had hoped to break the journey in Ajmer, but the city was closed to tourists. So was Pushkar. The election, which happened a couple of days ago without my noticing, has sparked a wave of Muslim riots, resulting in curfews. And this is well before the result is known – that takes weeks, but the favourites are the reactionary BJP, a party closely identified with Hindu fundamentalism, and tensions are running high. Sheikh, I remember was praying that the religiously neutral Congress Party would win, while Mohamd backs the extremists. This election worries me.

'Sir, you have a reservation?' asks the Samode Haveli receptionist in a way that tells me they are full. However, he does have a suggestion – another converted palace that once pushed his own into second place in a national league table.

Well, something must have changed. The first room I'm shown has a flooded bathroom, the second has scaffolding round the door, in the third, the beds are so short, I'll have to move a mattress on to the floor to sleep; but, if I delay any more, I'll never find an internet facility. I need to check whether there's anything from Robert.

'I know all the places,' says Opie and, for once, he comes up trumps. There is a small, dark 'computer café' just round the corner and I do indeed have a message. Robert has gone back to Udaipur, but he is keen on the idea of us working together and could start within a couple of months. He does, however, have all sorts of questions regarding my publishers, their sales and publicity networks and the delivery deadline that I'm working towards. My desire to sound upbeat has created the impression that things are vastly more advanced than they are in truth, and the enormity of the gap between his business-like imaginings and the floundering,

half-baked reality fills me with despondency. I don't even feel able
to reply.

Some folk dancing is scheduled in the garden, but it's chilly, so I
ask a waiter to light the nearby brazier.

'We are waiting for group, sir.'

'But it's cold. Can you light it now, please?'

He looks at his woodpile, wondering whether it will see him
through. 'Group is not here yet, sir.'

'No. I can see that. But I am. So will you light it now?'

Reluctantly, he strikes a match and goes off to rip a branch
from a tree. I wait for a while before asking what has happened to
the dancers – as if I didn't know.

'We are waiting for group, sir.'

'It says 7.30 in reception. 7.30 daily, group or no group.'

'Yes, sir. But today there is group.'

'And group is not here.'

'No, sir.'

I point to some tables laid up in the garden. 'Can I eat over
there?'

'Is for group, sir.'

'Not for hotel guests?'

'Sorry, sir.'

I go indoors to the restaurant, leaving the waiter wondering
anxiously whether to keep the fire going or douse it now and start
again later. An image of a busload of Japanese milling disconsolately
round the embers cheers me briefly, but the wait for my food in
the airless, empty dining room is interminable.

'Is anybody interested in the people actually staying in this
hotel?' I growl, at another waiter.

'Starter is coming, sir.'

'You said that half an hour ago. You said it again, ten minutes

later. Just bring me the main course. And I've asked you three
times to clear the cutlery from these other places...' He has,
however, disappeared to the garden, where a burst of drumming
heralds the coach party's arrival, so I hurl the offending implements
onto the sideboard.

It is, I admit, a less stoical gesture than I would have hoped for
at this juncture, but had I not been so mellowed by the last few
months I might have thrown them at the waiter.

No visual fanfare from sunlight streaming through Samode's jali
windows: today's landscape is hidden by rain clouds.

'How is family?' asks Vijay, bringing my bed-tea. He assumes
that I must, in the interim, have returned to England and I offer
some vague assurances regarding their welfare. 'Any tiger in
Ranthambore?' he continues brightly, as the downpour rattles on
the roof.

'In this weather?' I laugh, shaking my head.

'No walk today, sir, I think.'

'I can paint indoors,' I tell him contentedly; but the snag, as
usual, is the telephones. The lines are still down, which means no
progress report from Mohamd.

'Reading book about India?' asks Vijay, reluctant to brave the
elements.

'I usually am. But you may be able to help me…' The book is a
novel – not a very good one but, oddly enough, one in which a
couple of Opie's kinsfolk make a minor appearance. And here there
are no allusions to medieval royalty. These fictional Yadavs are
simply farmers: relatively low caste, yet politically powerful. So
where, I wonder, would that put them in relation to the Nayaks?
'Vijay, you said you didn't have the right background for university…
Do you mind if I ask?…' An Indian would have flushed this out
within seconds, but I can't help faltering. 'What caste are you?'

'We are potters, sir. Kumars. But today mostly young people doing other things.'

'Yet you still keep the potter's caste?'

'Of course, sir.'

'And the Nayaks, Vijay? Do you know about them? They're supposed to be camel breeders, aren't they?'

'Oh no, sir.' He smiles in puzzlement, but continues adamantly. 'In your country, I don't think you have this job, but here in India, when a father needs a wife for his son... maybe you have heard this... sometimes he sends a man to find a suitable girl.'

'You don't mean... surely not a marriage broker?'

'Sorry, sir. But yes, this is the man we call the Nayak. Not the camel-breeder.' He almost laughs, then checks himself. 'Is any problem?' he asks apologetically.

'No, it's fine,' I pretend, beaten yet again by the constant illusiveness of truth. 'Just that someone... someone I thought would know... told me differently.'

'This Mr Moon, he is very good person.' Opie offers this information to a total stranger, paying his bill at the same time as me. For several days, he has been furnishing the same appraisal to anyone half-way competent in English and it only makes me feel worse about how things have ended up: a better person would have found a way to like him again.

As we leave Samode, I feel an overwhelming sense that the heart of my trip is over. Neemrana will be just the beginning of the end. However, first there's the Opie lunch to get through. Even at my lowest ebb after Bhuj, there was a small speck of silver lining in the all-engulfing clouds: at least I wouldn't have to go for this meal. Now I do.

We stop at a private school near his village where he is paying for his children to be educated. They run to him with real devotion, their arms firmly locked around his trouser legs. The youngest won't let go, so he comes home with us for the afternoon. No one at the school seems to mind, or even notice.

Opie's family, in the broadest sense, constitutes the entirety of the village population of around two hundred. His house appears to be the largest: single storied, unadorned and box-like, but considerably more substantial than I expected. He has paid for a well, at which some relations are pumping water. He is also planning to finance a building for the government school, where some cousins are being taught in an open yard. It's extraordinary to see him here as the Lord of the Manor; and to think that so much of this hung by a thread, just a fortnight ago.

Mrs Opie has donned her best finery. The tinselled sari, like a cross between a birthday cake and a Christmas tree, must be immensely impractical for cooking. She doesn't join us, confining herself to the kitchen, but eight adults and some twenty children do join us. Not to eat, just to watch me eat. Even Opie merely watches, deferring his own lunch until I've finished.

It's embarrassing. Not just the sense of eating under a magnifying glass, but the knowledge that I ought to be performing a different script. This is meant to be the climax of some of the best weeks of my life with this man. I should be singing his praises without intermission. That's what these people usually hear and, as if to prompt me, Opie pulls out some dog-eared letters recording rapturous thanks for his services and company.

I have a questionnaire to complete for Mahtani, but I'll also put a letter with his parting tip. I'm not sure which is more difficult: how much to give or what to say? I've a lot to be thankful for, but I'm determined not to whitewash what happened in Gujarat. I'm not going to be softened up by Mrs Opie's second helpings.

★

Reorganising my luggage at Neemrana Fort, I found the box of biros, still more than half full: one of many bits of unfinished business. I put them near the waste paper basket, where they were quickly spotted by the bed tea boy. I told him he could take them and he ran off excitedly, dashing from courtyard to courtyard, handing 'one pen, one pen' to each of his delighted colleagues. I started a painting, but couldn't concentrate. I wandered listlessly round the battlements, a sinking, sad feeling filling my stomach. I watched Opie giving the car its most thorough wash, polish and dust in many months and finally settled on a rooftop terrace to watch the sunset.

'No message?' I ask a waiter serving tea.

'Village telephones outside order,' he says, so I resign myself to the view. Founded in 1464, the Fort was extended over five centuries to climb nine stories high up the hillside and the village must be two hundred feet below. An enormous plain stretches west towards the Aravallis, the mountains which have kept me company for so much of this journey. All that I have seen lies over there towards the reddening sun. And farthest west of all is Jaisalmer and Mohamd, getting no joy from the telephones… Except, of course, that he's not supposed to be in Jaisalmer. He should be in Delhi. If only he could call.

As smoke from village cooking fires drifts upwards, I try to draw some threads together: I've calmed down (more or less – there *was* that cutlery in Jaipur); I've developed some sides of myself that were stifled; and I've opened my mind to new ideas and people have taken me seriously; I still haven't answered the *big* question, but I'm much less afraid to let go…

'Sorry for disturb, sir. Village telephones…' The waiter has come to clear the tea things.

'Outside order,' I acknowledge regretfully.

'No, sir, now, sir, inside order. Urgent call coming downside.'

It is, as I assumed, Mohamd, but he is not, as I hoped, calling from Delhi. He's back in Jaisalmer. There was a surprise waiting for him and his father when they got home. 'They'd come from that village,' he says. 'The father of the girl, the one my brother was to marry. Also all her uncles and cousins. In fact, every adult man.'

'They found out?' I ask superfluously.

'While we were in Jodhpur,' he confirms. 'They'd made a kind of camp – thirty or forty peoples round the house. So many my mother had to cook for and always saying the food was not good enough. They wanted chicken and mutton and all these things but, before I came back, my mother had no money, so what could she do?'

'She could send your brother shopping,' is what I feel like suggesting, but instead I ask him what they want. Surely they can't now undo what his brother has done?

'They say they now need bigger dowry money, to get the girl a new husband. I've told them, later this year I can pay.'

'Your brother should pay,' I protest, as Mohamd's driving prospects fade.

'It's like I told you, he doesn't have a job. Anyway, that's not all. They say both me and younger brother must marry quickly.'

'The girls are too young. You said so yourself.'

'It do sometimes happen in villages.'

'But surely in this case…'

'They no longer trust us.'

'You mustn't give in.'

'It will ruin my family.'

'Can't you buy time?'

'I try this already. For three days I tell them, it's too soon. I

176

need one more year. Then I will do what they wish, but they say, "We don't believe you. We think you do like your brother..." But listen, I have to hurry. Not much money for telephone. What I wanted to ask...'

'I'll call you back.'

'Not possible in STD. What I need to know...'

'The Cottage Gallery!' I cut him short. 'I'll call you there.'

'I must go now to village. They are waiting for me. But tell me, if I have to marry this girl...'

'Be at the shop, same time tomorrow. We have to discuss this.'

'It was difficult already tonight...'

'Mohamd, just this once, just for twenty-four hours, put yourself first,' I implore him, but the line has gone dead.

'You are interesting in Rajasthan?' asks the Delhi bookseller. It took no time at all to find Nahar Singh's *Annals and Antiquities* and subsequent browsings have uncovered impossible quantities of useful material for the book project, but still he hopes to tempt me with one last volume. 'Here is rare book, no longer in printing.' He passes me a well-worn copy of *The Bhils of Rajasthan*. 'This number one edition, but I make good price.'

'Not for me,' I laugh, thinking history and art books are one thing, but an obscure work on aboriginal tribesmen! What do I need to know about their social organisation and marriage traditions? It's almost comically wide of the mark... Then, as I flick through the pages, I find a table listing all the various sub-tribes and there, printed in alphabetical order, is the name of Nayak. 'I'll take it,' I tell the shopkeeper.

It should have been obvious – the earrings on the Deogarh dancing boy, like those that Mohamd used to wear; the echoes of the Nayaks' home in the village near Poshina: all Bhils. The giveaway, of course, was the Bhil claim to fame for defending the

Maharanas, just as Mohamd said his own forebears had done. Yet I failed to make the connection. On a par with the untouchables then. Perhaps worse. And all of this clear from the outset to Opie Yadav. Yet so far from clear to me.

'*You have to be totally honest with me,*' I remember saying to Mohamd, when we talked about his finances on that camel ride.

'*I know that,*' I can hear him answering. '*I knew when you first wrote to me.*'

Why was it so difficult to share this truth about his name?

'Sir, I was calling my office,' says Opie, as we drive towards the Residency. 'Different driver coming to take you to airport. Me, tonight I drive to Jaipur. Tomorrow morning, meeting new guests – one English couple, two week tour…' Back to normality for him therefore. 'Our last drive,' he adds, in case I was slow on the uptake.

'You'll drive all night?' I feel unexpected sympathy, as I count some notes inside my wallet.

'After I see my wife,' he answers philosophically. 'You are happy with my services, sir? You remember Khajuraho?' he laughs nostalgically. 'You remember Camel Fair?' He doesn't ask if I remember Bhuj. 'You come back next year?' he continues, as I slide the appropriate cash into an envelope, alongside the carefully balanced letter that I wrote last night. 'This my number, sir.' He hands me a poorly printed card. 'Next time, no call Mahtani. These hotels I am booking. Charges very less.'

For a moment, I feel a surge of something close to affection. Just for an instant, I could tear up the letter, push a few extra notes into the envelope. Then I remember Mohamd.

'I have to hurry to make a telephone call,' I explain, to excuse myself from protracted expressions of gratitude on the Residency steps. It would be cheaper from a PCO, but a certain 'end of an era' recklessness has taken hold and I hasten inside, turning my back on Opie and the Ambassador.

There is a pleasing symmetry about arriving back where my travels began. I remember walking out through the urban fog, in search of dinner: an apprehensive figure on a concrete bridge, who now seems unreachably far away. Tonight I can pause in front of the bathroom mirror and say to myself: 'You look great. You feel great. You can do great things. All you have to do is decide.' It may not be true, but the greatest achievement of this journey is that it *feels* true! However, it is six o'clock.

Mohamd answers even before the first ring tone has finished. 'How was your tour today? Everything fine?'

'Never mind me,' I tell him briskly. 'Any news?'

'Still they are saying I must marry right now. But that's what I wanted to ask… I mean, supposing, for instance, they make me marry next weekend… Will you come?'

'Mohamd, I'm flying back to London tonight. I can't travel all the way back a week later.'

'There's a Jodhpur flight from Delhi. I could send a car…'

'I'm really sorry, I can't.'

'Riyaz also not here – gone to Mecca. I am thinking, if you and Riyaz not there, then I won't have big party, not till next time you come…'

'But surely none of this need happen. Why is it always you, giving in?'

I imagine myself in this situation, saying: 'Listen Dad, I have in my hand a letter to the bank, instructing them to cancel your standing order. Do you want me to sign it?' But Mohamd doesn't think that way.

'I have to do it,' he says simply. 'To save my family. If not, they are outcasts. No one will marry my younger brother.'

'Surely he could also find someone to marry for love.'

'Maybe,' he sighs. 'But it's worse than this. My three sisters, they all married men from same village, where the girls come from. Their husbands are there now at the house. If I refuse, they say they send back all my sisters. Nothing more to do with them. All their children too! Whole family outside society.'

'And they mean it?' I ask in shocked amazement.

'They mean it,' he answers grimly. 'Surely you can see? I can't do this to them. I can't ruin so many lives.'

'But all your plans?' I plead uselessly. 'Your visit to England?'

'Maybe after marriage…' He sounds defeated, as conscious as I am that his principal reason for coming was to break free from all this.

We go round the loop a second time, but the conclusion is the same and I try to change the subject. I thank him for all his help, for his loyalty, for all that I've seen through his eyes. I tell him India will never be the same, now that I have a friend here. What I don't do is ask about the letter. I think I know the answer to that one.

No caviar tonight. No champagne to fete a smooth take-off. I am right at the back of the plane, sharing a row of two seats with a sprightly widow, who has just had her first taste of India: a mere four days at the end of a cruise, but they have left her every bit as besotted as me. 'I don't think I'll ever be the same,' she laughs, half-embarrassed by her passion. 'I feel India has… I don't know… given me so much. You feel you want to put something back.'

It needs only this cue for me to tell her about Mohamd. With so much on my mind, I am glad to share it with a receptive audience.

'Poor boy,' she says, tutting disapprovingly at the arranged marriage.

'Our own system's not so great,' I suggest to her. 'Look at the divorce rate. Here, I've seen lots of cases where it works well. The other day, a Rajput princess told me, "It's essential for one's parents to do the research. Otherwise, one's husband might have a *completely* different attitude to servants!"' My neighbour chuckles on cue, but I am still not sure that she understands. 'It doesn't work for Mohamd because he's changed,' I continue. 'He's educated himself, worked hard to transcend the limitations of his background. His parents have enjoyed the economic benefits, but they failed to make allowances when it came to finding a bride. They hadn't noticed that he no longer fits in.'

'He's lucky,' she says, putting a motherly hand on my forearm. I was hoping to sound dispassionate, but she must have seen how emotional this makes me. 'He's found a good friend.'

'I'm the lucky one.' I try to laugh it off. 'I've got the friend, without the marriage.'

She changes the subject, enquiring how I could be free for so many weeks of travel, so I tell her how I came to leave the law. Then, inevitably, she asks what I plan to do next.

'I'm still uncertain,' I admit.

'You're very brave,' she says, as so many have before, and as usual I shrug this aside with a dismissive 'more like crazy'. Then she gives the conversation a twist, which it has never quite taken before. 'Aren't you worried,' she asks incisively, 'that – whatever it is you decide on – you might not be as successful as you were as a lawyer?' It's a question I have put to myself many times, without ever finding an answer that I wanted to face up to; but suddenly tonight I see things differently.

'Not at all,' I tell her confidently. 'You see, no one can take from me the success that I had in the law. Whatever happens, I'll always have that. Yet if I'd simply carried on, doing the same thing until retirement, my score of successes could only ever be *one*. This way, I've a chance to chalk up two, maybe three. Do you see? It can never be worse. It can never be fewer than it would have been if I hadn't made the break. There's really no downside.' My companion laughs with incredulity, but I press on excitedly: 'You remember how Mohamd was hoping that success in the West might "liberate" him – give him the freedom to live his life as he wanted? Well, what I've just realised – just *this minute* understood – is that my *own* success, my success in the *past*, has liberated *me*. It's made me *free to fail*.'

AFTER

Ten

'So, this is your book,' says Rana Nahar Singh, studying the cover with a frown.

'My first,' I explain. 'There are two.' I wait for some reaction, as he flips through the pages. I feel like one of his former pupils at Mayo College, handing in some ill-prepared homework. 'I'm sorry it's only a paperback,' I mumble defensively. 'The hard back sold out.'

'Congratulations,' he offers a little less sternly. 'I don't expect my own will do that.'

'You finished your work on the Deogarh miniatures?' I ask enthusiastically, but the frown has returned.

'This isn't about the palaces.' He sounds reproachful.

'It's about wine. About French wine. From the Languedoc.'

'Yes, I can see that from the title.' He turns the volume over to see what redeeming features the critics might have found in its favour. 'And the other?'

'Languedoc food. That's where I mostly live now…'

'After all your work on the palaces.' He shakes his head, as he must have done over so many schoolboy misdemeanours.

'I was part way through the palace book, with an agent, sending drafts off to publishers; but it wasn't a good time for books on India, what with earthquakes and tensions with Pakistan. You must have found tourism down?'

'We're usually busy,' he answers crisply, giving nothing away.

185

'Or so they tell me. I don't involve myself in that side.' I catch a fleeting glimpse of the proud Rajput prince behind the history teacher. 'Did you try any Indian publishers?' he asks, with a challenging stare.

'We tried everyone my agent could think of. Eventually one London editor said she wasn't really sure about the palaces, but she liked the way I wrote...' My voice trails away, as I watch him glance doubtfully at the opening lines of the wine book. 'It's not intended to be technical. It's meant to be...' The word 'fun' dies on my lips, as his forehead furrows. 'Would I have made "fun" out of the palaces?' he seems to be asking himself. 'She called me in,' I try to brazen things out. 'Asked me, was there anything else I'd like to write about. Well, by this time, I'd seen that Languedoc winemaking was going through some exciting changes...'

'Well, it's very kind of you,' says Nahar Singh, putting the volume aside with, I sense, very little intention of picking it up again. The interview appears to be over, but suddenly he relaxes, his manner warmer, less school-masterly, reflecting his latest incarnation as a hotelier. 'What are your plans for tomorrow? We could go for a jeep safari...'

'I'm sorry, I'm leaving for Jaisalmer in the morning. A friend of mine's collecting me.'

'Where's he sleeping? I don't think he's booked in here.'

'Somewhere nearby, I think.'

'But there isn't anywhere.'

'Some sort of motel, did he say?'

'Oh, *there*! On the highway. Well, it's better than sleeping in his car,' he adds, clearly doubtful about the company that I keep.

Mohamd was late.

He'd said we should leave at nine, but had promised to arrive by eight-thirty. However, it was already nine-fifteen and the receptionist was running out of small talk. I crossed to the parapet to watch for a likely looking Ambassador driving in through the outer gate, but the only sign of life was an elderly retainer raking the gravel.

I tried to piece together what I knew of Mohamd's life over the intervening five years. There hadn't been many letters – not in either direction, I had to admit. Yet we'd kept in touch, either by telephone or more recently by email. Never a December had passed without a call from him on Christmas Day, never a birthday without a card (latterly an e-card) bearing toe-curling verses on the subject of friendship; but these told me little about his state of mind.

'Motel only three kilometre far,' said the receptionist.

I was beginning to fear some mishap, when someone's big four wheel drive roared in, sending the gravel tidier hobbling to a place of safety. It stopped at the palace entrance about twenty metres below me and a portly, complacent-looking figure climbed down from the back seat. Taking his time, he ran both his hands through a thick mane of oily black shoulder-length hair and straightened a tweedy Nehru jacket over a plump stomach. Then, stiffly, he craned his neck to look up to where I was watching. It was Mohamd.

At least, I assumed so. But for the wave and the glance at his watch, I should never have known him.

'Sorry for late.' He emerged into the upper courtyard to hug me and, at this range, I recognised the smile, yet it was hard to credit such a change. 'Motel was full, so we slept in the car. Overslept,' he admitted with a yawn.

'Never mind,' I assured him, still reeling from the transformation. 'I don't fill in time sheets any more.'

He gave a puzzled smile, as he opened the car door for me. 'You don't mind that I brought a friend?... This is Narayan.'

A handsome figure in the front passenger seat stretched round to squeeze my hand in both of his. He had a neat moustache and wore another tweedy Nehru jacket like Mohamd's, except that his was a perfect fit for a lean, athletic frame. 'Sir, I wanted so much to meet you. Mohamd talking always about you. So much you know. So many good advices you give ...'

'And this is Ramesh...' The driver, a serene-looking figure of similar age, dressed in white trousers and loose matching top, gave a friendly nod, as he steered the car through the gate. 'You don't mind that we take this Toyota? It will be quicker, I think. Last night, we leave at nine-thirty, then stop for food, get to Deogarh by five o'clock.'

'So maybe Jaisalmer by five tonight?' I calculated.

'Definitely, I hope...' Mohamd's eyelids drooped for a moment, but he stirred himself again. 'How is Mr Andrew?'

'He's fine. He sends his best wishes. He rang me last night and reminded me...' I hesitated, uncertain whether to press the point so soon. 'Did you ever have the driving lessons?' I spared him the words 'which I paid for', but we both knew what I meant.

Mohamd looked sheepish. The answer was, after all, obvious. Why else would Ramesh be at the wheel? Yet the truth was more complex. 'Still I can't drive,' he mumbled, embarrassed. 'But I do have licence.'

'I hope the bribe cost less than the lessons.' I forced a laugh.

'How was your tour?' Mohamd changed the subject.

'Not really a tour, just one night in Udaipur and one in Deogarh... I came to see *you*.'

'You've come so far,' he said, embarrassed again.

'I gave up waiting for you to come to England,' I teased.

'It was difficult...' He looked away towards the side of the road. 'After marriage, it didn't seem...' His voice faded into thoughtful silence. Then his mobile gave an ear-splitting demonstration of its ringing tone. 'I bet you never thought you'd see these things working out here,' he laughed at the end of the call. 'But that was Ravi. You remember? His father has that shop in the *haveli*. Friday night he get married and he want to invite you. It will be good experience, I think. Something you have not seen.' He smiled, as if to forgive my failure to appear at a more important wedding.

'Definitely,' I told him, keen to make amends, as the mobile gave another shrill performance.

'It's Goppu,' said Mohamd, after a brief exchange. 'For you.'

'Good day, sir. How are you? I am very fine, thank you...' I hadn't heard Gajendra's warm effusive voice since we said goodbye in Bhuj, but it put an immediate smile on my face.

'It'll be great to see you,' I enthused. 'And my friends, arriving on Saturday, they're really looking forward to meeting you.'

'Ah yes, sir, Mr Alex, Mrs Elektra...' Gajendra turned more cagey. 'You want I escort them on Sunday and Monday, right? Because Mumda drive with you, down to Jodhpur airport. He asked me yesterday, but...' I flashed my friend a look of annoyance. He was supposed to have fixed this weeks ago. 'Local agency booked me already those days. I am so sorry, sir. But has Mumda told you? Now I have restaurant here in Jaisalmer. Veg, Non-Veg, Beer, Wine... Please, you and your friends, you must all come for dinner.'

'Don't worry,' said Mohamd, when the call was finished. 'I've arranged someone else. I'm sure your friends they like.'

A third piercing jingle prevented me from testing the proposition, but this time it was a very different call. Mohamd spoke softly, affectionately, his voice caressing the other party. A sense of tact demanded dialogue with Narayan. 'You work also as a guide?' I asked, thinking of Alex and Elektra.

'Not like Mumda,' he said regretfully. 'You know, sir, now he works through all Rajasthan? Also Delhi and Agra. Often with groups, many times big Spanish groups!' Narayan could not have sounded more proud, if he'd been Mohamd's father. 'But not me. Mostly I just make desert tours. Very much I hope we make camel safari, you and me. This will be great honour for my side. And Mumda, these days, he doesn't go so much by camel,' Narayan chuckled, patting his hard, straight stomach, with a wink at his friend's bulging waistline.

'Too much of beer,' Mohamd admitted, having finished his call.

'Beer?' I queried, recalling his father's prohibition. 'Things really have changed.'

'Sometimes also rum.'

'No need to apologise. I drink wine nearly every day.'

'You write your book about wine,' said Narayan admiringly. 'Mohamd show me when you send.'

'Have you read it?' I asked him, joking.

'Till now, only first hundred pages,' he answered, wholly serious. 'For me, very hard, but always we show to tourists. Many times they say, "So much we are liking wine. In England, we buy this." '

'I'll watch for the sales surge,' I laughed.

'And your food book. This we are also showing. So much you know, sir.'

'No more writing palace book?' asked Mohamd and I explained again how I found myself side-tracked into the Languedoc. However, he still looked disappointed. 'Many weeks you came to Rajasthan, many palaces researching…'

'But never made it to Jaisalmer,' I admitted. 'There didn't seem to be a suitable palace. And do you remember? You were planning to meet me in Jaipur, then your mother got sick…' Even as I said this, I knew it was I who should have made more effort. I had already fallen back into old bad habits, letting my work rule the day, yet this wasn't what was worrying him.

'I hope you don't mind,' he began hesitantly. 'When you asked me to book your hotel…'

'Killa Bhawan, yes.'

'I thought good surprise would be Mandir Palace. Since last few years, it is made like hotel. Good researching, I was thinking, but now I don't know.'

'I'm sure it'll be great.' I swallowed my disappointment and we continued in awkward silence.

At the edge of a busy market town, Ramesh spoke for the first time, asking something of Mohamd and pointing to his watch. It was only mid-morning and we were still far from Jodhpur, but presumably they had all missed breakfast. 'You are feeling maybe little bit hungry?' asked Mohamd. To judge from the brawny quartet washing their hands at a tap in the street, the chosen establishment catered mainly to lorry drivers, but Ramesh had his eye on the last unoccupied expanse of formica. 'It is fine for you, I think,' said Mohamd, setting off across the street for some mineral water, and I watched him dodging the traffic at his measured, almost stately pace. He couldn't be more than twenty-four or five and was only moderately overweight, yet he moved with the ponderous, wide-legged waddle of an older and fatter man.

'Do you ever see Opie,' I asked, when he returned.

'Once or twice,' he responded, without elaborating.

'I saw Mr Sheikh in Udaipur. He said Opie no longer works for Mahtani. When Sheikh filed his report, when Mahtani learned what had happened, he said Opie had to go.'

'He got the sack?' asked Mohamd, sounding concerned.

'He got no pay rises. And mostly Indian tourists, so very little shopping. Eventually he took the hint. Less messy than dismissing him. Now he just gets occasional work, when somebody's short of a driver.'

'Do you think he has enough for his family?'

'Enough to get by. But he won't be building the school that he was planning.'

Mohamd fell pensively silent, leaving me to what I now found were very mixed emotions.

'And how was Mr Sheikh?' Mohamd resumed brightly. 'Since few years back, I don't see him, but last time in Udaipur his office look closed.'

'He's had problems,' I answered, as we returned to the Toyota. 'He took on his son as a business partner in the travel agency, and the son had big ideas, plans for expansion. He persuaded Sheikh to borrow too much money. It might have been all right, if the son hadn't been so lazy, neglecting his side of the work, preferring the good life... In the end, they had to close. Now the likes of Mahtani send their business elsewhere.'

'He was a good man,' Mohamd said quietly; then he and Narayan fell asleep, while Ramesh played some jangly Indian pop music, as if to keep himself awake. Certainly, for a while, it kept me awake; then I nodded off as well.

I'm rudely woken by the bleating of sheep. We have pulled off the road and are surrounded by vehicles, which have either their bonnets open or their wheels jacked up. Amongst them is an open-backed truck, laden with shepherds and sheep. The animals, to judge by the noise, seem to share my dismay at the news of a puncture, but their masters seem completely unperturbed by our jumping of the queue. 'Only one hour,' says Ramesh, as a mechanic starts the repair, but the hour passes slowly, the conversation desultory. Then oddly, as soon as we are back on the road, Mohamd over-compensates with a barrage of questions about the years since we saw each other. The interrogation is, however, short-lived. Within half an hour we have a second flat tyre.

At least this time we've stopped in a village. It is unremarkable, almost indistinguishable from so many that I've wandered round before, but today, through Mohamd's eyes, I learn how segregated and stratified such apparently simple communities can be: 'Here is street for barber caste.' (I had never imagined that hair-cutting might be anything but a simple career choice, still less that those who practised it would be herded together.) 'And here street for garland-maker caste.' (I had never seen garland production as a *career*, let alone as a caste, requiring everyone born into it to live side by side. Indian estate agency must be every bit as complicated as marriage-broking.)

It's well after dark when we finally see the floodlit Jaisalmer Fort. I can't wait to go to the Trio, but Mohamd asks to be excused. He says he has no appetite, yet I sense that the real reason may be the latest in the line of whispered phone calls.

'But we haven't really talked about your family situation...'

'We have three days,' he reminds me, looking relieved to be departing.

I'm not sure which contributed most to my sleepless night, the smell of mothballs or the thinness of the single blanket; or maybe it was just the all-night counterpoint from a pair of barking dogs. By sunrise I was finding my way up to the Killa Bhawan doorbell.

'I know you,' said Manu, the guru. 'You are friend of Mumda, no?' He was wrapped in a blanket and I thought for a moment I'd dragged him from his bed. Then I remembered, this was his usual attire for serving breakfast. 'Yes, I have room,' he said. 'I have en suite room. But after tomorrow, no en suite. Shared bathroom only...' It needed but a second's hesitation to see that no facilities at all would be better than no sleep. I just had to break the news to Mohamd.

'It's not a problem,' he assured me, but I sensed that it *was* a problem, when I learned there was nothing for me to pay at the Mandir Palace. He was planning to make this his treat and the more he insisted that he hadn't already paid in advance, the more I doubted this.

Back at Killa Bhawan, Mohamd's mentor had a dog-eared letter he wanted his more literate disciple to decipher, so I settled on the rooftop terrace to listen to the songs wafting up from some infant musicians near the Fort entrance. They were too far away to be certain, but surely the singer sounded just like the Bikaner boy and I was blissfully drifting off to sleep, when Mohamd came to break the spell: 'Riyaz invite us to lunch.'

It was only eleven o'clock, yet he was plainly keen to leave and his motorbike (he now had his own) was soon roaring rudely through the densely populated streets.

'Ravi's place. They're preparing for marriage,' he shouted, as we whizzed past a building decked with fairy lights, making no concessions to the carter unloading catering equipment. Nor was any thought spared for the musician boys, choked in dust by the gate. Only on sighting friends did he screech to a more sociable halt.

'Hello, Mr Patrick,' said countless young men, whom I'd never met.

'Welcome to Jaisalmer, sir,' said an older passer-by, shaking Mohamd's hand.

'You know so many people,' I marvelled, already feeling a warm sense of belonging.

'People say I should be politician,' he laughed and, for a moment he reminded me of a celebrated untouchable turned minister of state, pictured in yesterday's newspaper – except that the look-alike had just been arrested on corruption charges, having allegedly bought his way into power.

'Sir, Most Welcome To New Cottage Gallery.' I looked round to let Mohamd enter first, but he was busy with a phone call, so I went in alone to find the new establishment looking much like the old, although – surprisingly – slightly smaller. Riyaz himself seemed unchanged, apart from the odd grey hair. He quizzed me, first on the success of my tour, then on the wellbeing of myself and my family and Mr Andrew. Then he updated me on his own situation: 'You Know, Sir, Now I Have Wife. Also Small Son. Later You Will See…' Then with the preliminaries out of the way, he turned to the main agenda item: the New Cottage Gallery Stock. 'This Best Quality,' he insisted, producing a succession of shawls, surely indistinguishable from the Old Cottage Gallery Stock. 'I Tell You Honestly, Sir, You Not Find Like This…'

'Very nice for ladies,' I suggested, but Riyaz was undetetered.

'Now We Have New Line – Jackets Also.' He flourished a black example with a Nehru collar. 'No Need To Buy. Just You Feel The Quality.' As he coaxed my arms into the sleeves, I noted it was exquisitely embroidered, black on black, in silk. Impossibly frivolous on my writer's royalties, yet with one of these, I could throw out my stuffy old dinner jacket… Before I could ask the price, he'd draped a black silk scarf round my neck. 'This Very Elegant, I Tell You Honestly, Sir.'

'How much is it? The jacket, I mean.'

'Very Less, Sir. But This Combination Very Perfect For You. Because All What You Do For The Mumda, Just You Buy The Jacket. Scarf I Like To Give.'

'What would be your best for the jacket, without the scarf?'

'Scarf Is Best Quality. Better, I Think, You Wear The Both, Sir. Scarf Is The Perfect…'

It seemed a triumph to buy only the jacket but now, sitting cross-legged in Riyaz's flat, I calculate how little I can have saved by foregoing the complete ensemble.

The flat is also new but, like the shop, seems slightly smaller than its predecessor, with equally minimal furnishings. Lunch has been cooked by Riyaz's wife but only Riyaz, Mohamd and myself are eating. Even Riyaz's brother merely hovers like a waiter, while the wife sits plumply in a corner, holding their two year old son on her lap. The boy looks tired, not quite 'with us', his head lolling sideways, but he manages a smile. The two of them are just back from Delhi, Riyaz explains. From Delhi hospital. The boy has to go there once a month. He has leukaemia.

Riyaz shows me the medical reports. It's the best hospital in India for this illness. He quotes a breathtaking sum – even by English standards – as the cost of the treatment, yet still he wants my opinion. Might there be anything better in England?

'Every rupee Riyaz earn he spend on medicine and train fares,' Mohamd whispers. 'Always they travel first class because the boy is so sick. Imagine the house they could build with this much money.'

I shake my head sadly. I've not been much help on the medical reports, but at least I bought the jacket. However, the boy seems upset. He has started to cry and is pointing at me. I smile what I hope is a soothing smile but the boy shakes his head angrily. Riyaz tries to calm him down, but without success, and his mother carries him out from the room.

'He Think You Are Doctor,' says Riyaz.

'You mean he was frightened?' I ask apologetically.

'No Sir, He Think You Bring Us New Medicine,' says Riyaz. 'Always He Hope For New Medicine. I Explain Him, This Is Only Mumda's Friend. Then He Cry.'

It should have been a good chance to talk: an aimless potter round the lake, away from his motorcycle, away from his friends, away from anything that he hadn't shown me before. I'd even persuaded him to switch off the mobile. I wanted to understand how he felt about his marriage but, whenever I tried, he changed the subject. However, on the way back to town, he gave me a kind of answer. He took me to a down-at-heel hostel, showing me the room that he was renting with a trio of guides. I saw the double bed on which three out of the four took turns to sleep; the cold stone floor for the unlucky one.

'And your wife?' I asked him, dismayed at these arrangements.

'She lives in village, with my parents.'

'How often do you see her?'

'Sometimes one, maybe two times a month.' He plainly preferred not to pursue the topic, driving me instead to a building site on a dusty, potholed street near the city's edge. 'This my father's land,' he explained. 'You remember we met him here, that day we took camels? There was one small house, where my brother lived. Now I build new house for family. One room for parents. One for older brother, wife and two daughters. Also one…' he hesitated, then continued without enthusiasm, 'for me and wife.'

The plot was barely two metres wide and, although it ran back nearly ten metres from the road, it was hard to imagine so many people inside. Little more than the ground floor walls had been built, but some rusting steel supports projecting skywards implied plans for a second storey. The street-side façade was clad with ill-fitting sections of local yellow sandstone, somewhat crudely carved in imitation of the city's *havelis*, but it looked as if work had been halted quite some time ago.

'I think this good for my wife,' Mohamd explained. 'She never lived in city. My brother's wife, I think I told you, she is city girl, from Ajmer – more modern. What I hope, with her help, slowly, slowly, my wife start to live differently. Also, my parents. Slowly, slowly, grow like city people. You see, when I have children, I want better start for them.' The talk of children was encouraging, but his prospects of fatherhood were clearly prejudiced by the nights in his hostel. 'My parents complain always no grandson,' he admitted.

Night was starting to fall as the motorcycle stopped again inside the Fort. 'Come,' he said, climbing some steps towards a sign reading 'Cyber Café'. 'More of my friends you can meet.'

The only sign of internet activity was a gap-year student, sat at one of only two computers in a small back room. His gap-year girlfriend was the centre of attention in a larger room at the front, where a number of Mohamd's contemporaries lay sprawled on some fabric-draped mattresses. A burning joss stick, a languid CD and a pink-tinted light bulb completed the attempt at decadence. Two of the lads shuffled sideways to make room for us on their mattress. Satish, the young owner, sent the most junior of the group out for beers. Mohamd quickly disappeared to the street, clasping his mobile to his ear, so it fell to the least salubrious of the company to look after me.

'Tanu, sir.' He thrust his three-day stubble closer for better eye contact. 'Spanish guide.'

'Like Mohamd,' I answered, stepping back a pace.

'No one like Mumda,' said Tanu. His garbled account of the way in which Mohamd had first identified the dearth of local Spanish speakers was hardly news: I had paid for his Delhi language course myself. And I knew he'd either charmed or bribed his way into the Spanish travel agencies to win their lucrative tour groups. What I hadn't heard about was how he'd then taken Tanu and another younger boy under his wing. Tanu's English was becoming increasingly hard to decode, but the gist appeared to be that the two of them had 'shadowed' our mutual friend, just as he had 'shadowed' Manu, until they could stand on their own as the city's only other Spanish-speaking guides. 'But Mumda number one,' Tanu emphasised, loyal to the end.

'So you've got to know each other,' said Mohamd, rejoining us. 'Did Tanu tell you? It's him I've booked for Mr Alex and Elektra.'

'Alex is a hard man to please!' I whispered, as Tanu drifted away to slump on a mattress.

'Tanu doesn't get so much work...'

'Maybe he could take Gajendra's assignment.'

'We'd have to ask local travel agent.'

'Or I could go to Jodhpur on my own. Then you'd be free yourself...'

'You worry too much,' he chided affectionately. 'It's time to eat. But first I want to ask you one thing. At the restaurant, please, you mustn't mind, if... Sometimes, after one, two drinks...' Before he could complete the thought, his mobile rang again and he headed for the computer room.

'One more beer, sir?' pressed Satish hospitably and I almost accepted. I could happily pass the whole evening in this convivial haven, but there was a more pressing objective. I quickly drained my glass and hurried outside and down to the gate, where the musician boys were packing up.

'No more songs?' I asked plaintively, and they shook their heads. Then the smaller one pointed to an elderly man, sitting smoking at a distance, as he counted the afternoon's takings. 'No more music?' I proffered him a banknote.

'Restaurant,' he grunted, meaning presumably their next engagement.

'Five minutes?' I tried a larger denomination, but the man simply shrugged and applied himself to his cigarette. By now, I was determined that the boy should sing. I doubled the sum on offer and there was an agonising pause. Then at last the minder nodded. The younger boy tapped a lively rhythm on his *tabla*, while the other started pumping out the melody on his harmonium. Finally he sang.

And yes, it *was* like the Bikaner boy! His wild, whooping voice filled the square. It cut through the evening air, sharp as steel; yet

its earthy warmth matched the sunset glow on the ramparts. Every
trilling note had a passion that was way beyond his years. Every
dancing phrase had a smile in it. The tabla player drummed harder,
his tiny body convulsed in the beat, as he urged the singer on to
greater fervour. The wailing refrain from the squeeze-box spiralled
ever more nimbly round the vocal line. The singer closed his eyes,
nodding ecstatically to the pulse of his song, his rough, ragamuffin
features briefly transfigured into beatific serenity.

'I'm sorry,' says Mohamd, catching up with me. 'I think tonight
you are feeling boring.'

'I knew he'd never go to England,' sighs Gajendra. 'Mohamd is my
very good friend, sir, but he is also lazy.'

I'm sitting with the young restaurateur in his new
establishment. It opened six months ago, but already the Jaisal
Treat is flourishing. Tonight more than forty out of sixty covers are
taken, mostly by tourists recommended by other guides. He is
looking for larger premises, even contemplating a guest house.
And all this in the evenings, after his days as the VIPs' favourite
guide.

We've been reminiscing about Gujarat. Time has let Gajendra
see it all as a comic adventure. He's been chuckling away
nostalgically, as if at his dearest memories, and even I saw the
funny side, as he treated me to his good-natured mimicry of Opie
and Sheikh. More sombrely, we've recalled how full of promise
everything had seemed, how certain Mohamd had been that, if
only he could make it to England, everything would be fine.

'Sorry, sir, now I must be going.' Gajendra is suddenly in a
hurry. 'To see my wife and daughter. Mumda told you I have one
daughter since May-time, yes? Doing very fine... But sir, you've
had no food!' He rattles off some instructions to a waiter, then
makes as if to leave. 'Sir, I hope, if you like the food, you and your

friends will all come for dinner when they arrive on Saturday – your last night, I think.'

'Thanks. I'm sure we'd like that. But you were saying about Mohamd, how you never thought he'd come to England…' Gajendra hesitates, stealing a glance at his friend who, with Tanu, is propping up the bar. 'I know he always said he was lazy, but he'd achieved such a lot on his own.'

'He could have so much more work, if he wanted,' says Gajendra, sitting down again to talk more confidentially. 'Always I tell him, he should finish that house, bring his family here, give his children a good education, not let them end up selling fossils, breaking stones…'

'The work on the house seems to have stopped.'

'He has money problems, many debts…' Gajendra breaks off, as Mohamd approaches, his gait suggesting rather less Pepsi than rum in his tumbler.

'The best food in Jaisalmer,' he mumbles, as he steadies himself on the back of a chair; then, with an effort of concentration: 'Has Goppu told you? About Mr Alex and Mrs Elektra?'

Gajendra apologises. We were so busy catching up. However, he has managed to wriggle out of his Sunday commitment, so can do their city tour; but the Monday camel safari is still out of the question and Narayan, the obvious choice, has a wedding commitment, so Mohamd is planning to travel back from Jodhpur during Sunday night to take the assignment himself. However, the dazed look in Mohamd's eye inspires little confidence in this proposal.

'About his debts,' I whisper, as he returns to his cronies.

'Forgive me, sir, I should not have mentioned this.'

'I'm glad you did. I'm trying to understand. When I sent him the money for his Spanish lessons, I told him it was a gift, but he insisted on taking it as a loan. Now you say he owes other people money?'

'Too many,' says Gajendra sadly. 'I lent him a little myself, just to help pay the interest on his big loan for the house. I don't mind if he doesn't pay me back. It's not the money, it's… Well, you've seen him for yourself. But tell me…' He is now about to leave in earnest. 'You are liking the food?'

'It's the best place in town,' I tell him sincerely.

'Better than Trio?'

'Only one thing wrong,' I tease him. 'The name. You should call it Duo.'

Gajendra laughs but shakes his head. It's the Trio's owner who keeps him in guiding work.

'Good news!' says Manu, joining me on the rooftop, huddled in his usual blanket. 'Cancellation. Tomorrow you keep en suite, only next day share.' I tell him not to worry either way and he sits companionably at my breakfast table. 'So, you are Mohamd's friend,' he says thoughtfully.

'Yes,' I laugh, uncertain what he is thinking, but conscious that I can't have been much of a friend to have waited so long to come back.

'Mohamd has many friends,' adds Manu enigmatically. 'He help many people. Sometimes too many people.'

Before I can ask what he means, some other guests call him to their table and I wander across to the parapet, looking down onto a neighbouring roof terrace, where a boy of about ten is busy combing his sleek black hair.

'You are friend of guide?' he calls, sparing me barely a look as he perfects his parting in a mirror. 'Friend of Mumda?'

'Yes. How do you know?'

'I know everything. I am Sadhu.' Still no glance in my direction. 'What your job in England?' He gives me a first challenging stare, as if defying me to impress him.

'I'm a writer.' He looks blank and I mime the business of writing.

'Newspaper?'

'Books.' I imitate the act of opening one, then turn the tables: 'What's your father's job?'

'My father is dead already,' he answers bluntly, almost daring me to come out with some tritely compassionate response. 'I work in shop,' he continues brightly. 'Now I get ready.' There follows some more combing but, remarkably, no invitation to the shop and he leaves without a goodbye.

'Mohamd late,' says a passing Manu and I settle resignedly to watch the succession of tourists approaching the Fort. I see the musicians set themselves up for another day's fund-raising. I spot Gajendra, marshalling a crocodile of elderly ladies in stentorian French – the ring in his voice telling me they clearly don't share his focussed attitude to life. Then finally Mohamd, cruising sedately into the square on his motorcycle. He pauses for a chat with a handsome, curly-haired youth. He takes out his wallet and passes the younger man a wad of notes. Then, in no particular hurry, he points his bike towards the gate.

'Sorry for late.' He puffs his way up to the rooftop. 'Last night I go to village.'

'You saw your wife?' There are worse excuses for delay.

'No, right now with her own parents. But I think you like to see her, no? Tomorrow we can go, after I speak to her father. Today I am thinking we go to my village. New village. Not where you came before.'

'You're sure you shouldn't speak to *your* father first?' I picture the forbidding figure in the army trench coat, still unconvinced that I'm a suitable companion for his son.

'Only my mother and younger brother are there. And already I asked my mother. She will be very happy.'

On the open road, Mohamd's top speed is probably no more than sixty kilometres per hour, yet to me it feels excitingly fast, rejuvenatingly fast. I haven't done this since I was *his* age and could almost sing for the joy of it. But there are serious matters to attend to.

The pillion might not seem an obvious place for a difficult conversation. Much of my questioning will be blown away, likewise most of Mohamd's hoarse replies, yet the lack of eye contact makes it easier. I broach the topic of the building project, indeed his finances generally, and learn that he's pinning his hopes on a film to be shot here in Jaisalmer by some Italians. They need a translator. Indeed, they need more than a linguist; they need a fixer, someone who can oil the right wheels. He reminds me that he knows a lot of people. However, the catch seems to be that he must use his own money to grease a palm or two, before the Italians will confirm the project.

'Be careful,' I warn him, but my words are no doubt lost on the wind. In any case, his attention has been grabbed by a small encampment at the roadside, where three or four families have erected some flimsy-looking windbreaks, made from desert vegetation. They have no form of overhead protection, nothing to shelter them from sunshine or rain, nothing to safeguard their paltry possessions. Some grubby infants run towards us, waving, trying uselessly to keep pace with the bike.

'You see those places?' shouts Mohamd. 'That's how my father lived when he first came from Pakistan. For me, for my brothers and sisters, it was never like this. Like I told you that time, I owe him more than you think.'

We stop beside a rough enclosure, set a few metres back from the dirt-track road. Its walls, about as high as my shoulders, have been crudely patched together with a confusion of stone, twigs and mud. Beyond them are the bare, flat roofs of some brutal concrete cubes. The only sign of life is a scrawny goat, tethered to a metal post that may once have supported a road sign.

'Three years before, this I build for my family,' says Mohamd, kicking the goat aside and pushing at the makeshift gate. Inside, there are two young women, busy with domestic chores, but as soon as they see me, they scurry off to cower in an open-fronted storeroom. Less timid, an older woman, rake-thin and stooping, rises from the lump of stone where she was sitting in the shade.

Mohamd's mother has changed. The rattling white bangles still hide her upper arms, but the chain linking nostril to ear lobe has gone and her down-sized earrings would not look out of place on Elektra. More importantly, she is no longer veiled and her smile is one of genuine warmth. She speaks to Mohamd, who quickly interprets: 'She's making food, but it's not quite ready. Shall I show you round?'

His gesture embraces the yard, with its handful of randomly sited buildings. Apart from the store, there are two whitewashed concrete structures side by side, each with a steel door and a pair of small unglazed windows, divided by a metal bar. Neither can be more than a single room. Slightly farther off, is a thatched construction, made of mud mixed with cow dung, reminiscent of the old family home, and, like its predecessor, decorated with simple painted patterns: his parents' place, Mohamd explains. The concrete quarters are assigned to him and his elder brother, with their wives, leaving nowhere, as far as I can see, for the younger brother and the corresponding bride.

Before I can ask about their fate, Mohamd steers me into his own accommodation. The interior has been painted a deep, submarine sea-green and it takes a moment for my eyes to adjust. There is, however, little to see, just a big steel trunk, a blanket-covered *charpai*, barely large enough for two, and a few Bollywood movie stills taped to the walls: more a bachelor bed-sit than a matrimonial suite. He drags something from beneath the bed – some pieces of fractured marble in a bilious brownish-yellow. 'It was meant to be a present,' he explains, joining the pieces together to make a drinks table. 'I have to get another... find a way to send to England.' Then he opens the padlocked trunk. 'In case of bandits,' he says and shows me two neatly ordered piles of possessions, the larger one his, the forlornly small one his wife's. On the top of his own lies a pristine passport, never used; next to it the binoculars that I gave him. 'You remember?' He smiles at the memory of their rooftop use, then takes up a photograph album. 'Shall we go outside to look?'

Plates of spicy millet dumplings are waiting for us on a *charpai* in the courtyard. Fidgeting near them, as if hoping for leftovers, is a moody looking adolescent. Without exactly introducing him, Mohamd explains that this is his younger brother. Nodding vigorously, the brother beckons me to follow him. In the narrow gap between the perimeter fence and his elder siblings' residences, he has slung a tarpaulin to make a roof over his own rickety *charpai* and metal trunk. 'I and wife,' he says proudly.

Back in the courtyard, a crowd of adult males has gathered round the food – neighbours, more curious than hungry, it would seem – and their closely pressed noses do nothing for my dexterity with the dumplings. I'd gladly surrender them to the brother, were it not for Mrs Nayak homing in on me to monitor my appreciation. 'I had a big breakfast,' I whisper and Mohamd quickly gives what sounds like an order. Smiling serenely, his mother clears everything away.

'What about your older brother?' I ask, as Mohamd pours water from a jug over my sauce-stained hands. 'Did he ever get a job?'

'He's teaching,' says Mohamd, picking up the album. 'In next village. The place he always wanted.'

The photos are methodically organised in chronological order. There's nothing from his early childhood (no access to cameras in those days) and the oldest snap, now curling and faded, shows Mohamd aged eleven, sitting wide-eyed in a restaurant, as dazzled by the experience as he is by the flash. 'First time I eat with knife and fork,' he explains. 'One English tourist invite me.' Next is a grainy print of a teenager, posing self-consciously on the steps of a cinema. On the facing sheet, is a youthful Gajendra, striking a mock-heroic attitude beside a movie billboard. 'First time we go to Jodhpur...' He breaks off, embarrassed: the fourth photo shows him looking vulnerable on a bed in his singlet and underpants, flexing barely visible biceps. 'One small guesthouse we stayed in,' he mutters, moving swiftly on through the other Jodhpur sights.

Next come the pictures I sent from England: Andrew and Mohamd in the desert; Mohamd and me loaded with Cottage Gallery purchases; the three of us on Ravi's rooftop, perhaps with the distant girl in the background. In all of these, a wiry adolescent wears the same childish T-shirt that I know from a photo on my desk; then a leap of a year to the dapper young man of my second visit, still strikingly slim, but impeccably tailored and groomed.

A series of Gujarat souvenirs ends with the four of us in the Prince Hotel, the last time I saw Mohamd: the night we learned of his engagement, when somehow he convinced us this was merely a detail to be worked around; the night when Opie planned to set his trap, yet none of us knew this yet. For the moment, the photograph speaks of simple, unclouded happiness, the joy of a new and improbable friendship... A friendship I've badly neglected in the intervening years. *Where have I been while so much changed?*

A turn of the page takes us to the Himalayas for his one and only holiday: a trekking expedition, made with five male friends. To judge from the trimness of his waistline, this must have been soon after Gujarat and therefore soon after his marriage, a belated stag party in lieu of a honeymoon perhaps. 'My best friends,' says Mohamd, as I study the grinning line-up. 'Except for Riyaz in shop. And you in England.' Gajendra, Ravi and Tanu are easily recognised. Another must be Narayan, without his moustache. Only the final figure – the youngest and best-looking of the team – is new to me. Yet there is something familiar, something in the smile... Before I can ask, the focus shifts to Kashmir and the wedding of Riyaz. Both Mohamd and Gajendra wear shiny, flashily cut suits but Mohamd has put on several pounds since the tailor took his measurements and his well oiled hair is almost collar length. 'No more after this,' he says, flicking pensively through empty pages, as a single loose photo of himself and Gajendra falls from the back. 'Gajendra's marriage,' he tells me off-handedly and replaces it before I can look.

'Nothing from your own marriage?' I ask, as Mohamd closes the album.

'No, it's like I told you, with Riyaz in Mecca and you in England, I didn't make big party. Goppu, I think, took some pictures.' He thinks for a moment, then extracts a tiny, almost passport-sized photo from his wallet. 'I have only this.' In the place that was once reserved for the boy, the young protégé that he used to call... what was it? Pepsi?... he now has a head and shoulders image of himself and his wife.

'The same suit,' I observe, lost for any other words. The marital photograph might easily be a prison mugshot of the latest detainees. Certainly the expressions could hardly look more resigned, more condemned. In other respects, Mohamd looks exactly as I remember him: the suit fitting comfortably, the hair neatly trimmed, the features still boyishly fresh. His wife is half-hidden by the veil of the red and gold sari worn by all Rajasthani brides, her face further obscured by the silver chain looped from earlobe to nose. Her eyes look shyly downwards, away from the camera, yet there is no mistaking the lack of joy in them.

I remember Elektra asking me, 'But what about the wife? Have you thought about her in all of this?'

'It's my friend I'm concerned about,' I insisted. 'He's the one whose future's been wrecked.' But now I see the other side. Here are two lives rendered unhappy.

In the Cyber Café, a glaring striplight has banished the mood of languorous ease; the music tonight is more upbeat and purposeful; and the lads, who yesterday lolled lethargically on the mattresses, now sit cross-legged and alert. Each has a pile of printed cards, which he's stuffing into envelopes, as Satish, the young proprietor, bustles round to check on progress. 'Eight hundred invitations,' he explains. 'My sister was getting married twelve days from now. Eight hundred invitations already we have sent, but now the astrologers change their minds, say this not auspicious time, they must be married in five days' time. So new invitations we deliver tonight, some even as far as Jodhpur.'

'Too much of marriages,' sighs Tanu. 'Tomorrow, seven invitations already I have, between ten and midnight.'

'It's the season,' says Mohamd, plainly holding just as many.

'Is it always the night that's auspicious?' I ask, hoping to limit my revels to Ravi's.

'No, for me they said ten in the morning, but I think they got it wrong!'

Satish is about to conscript him for the mailshot, but he's saved by his mobile. The call is another of his *sotto voce* dialogues, for which he favours the back room, so I offer to lend a hand myself. Few of the young men speak English, but I'm rapidly, uncomplicatedly absorbed into the collective effort. 'Like brothers,' says a stranger, putting a welcoming arm round my shoulder and, for all the superficiality of the gesture, I feel a surge of emotion: I've never, in all my time in India, felt such a sense of belonging.

'You eat at Gajendra's?' asks Tanu, wiping sweat from his brow.

'Yes, but only if he lets me pay. Not like last night.'

'Goppu make very good business,' Tanu answers, as if that justified any amount of scrounging.

'Shall we…?' Mohamd has finished his call and I follow him into the street; but there's a change of plan: 'Do you mind if we go to that girl's house?' He pauses, uncertain whether I've understood. 'The girl on the roof.'

'You mean, you still see her?'

'Not every day. She lives with her family. But just now, I spoke to her. Only her father is there. Mother gone to Udaipur.'

'Maybe *after* the restaurant?' I feel I need for some time to fit this new information into place.

'She wants to make dinner for us. But first I have to buy present for her father.' Mohamd slows his motorbike beside a liquor store.

'Should I bring something?' I ask, as he reappears with a bottle of Indian whisky.

'This is fine,' he assures me, then points bashfully to four letters painted just below the motorcycle's handlebars: M U S A. 'You see these? It's like a code. No one else knows, but to you I can tell… M U is for Mumda, S A for Salu. That's what I call her. Her real name is Prithi.' (He pronounces this 'Pretty'.) 'But always my pet name is Salu.'

'What do her parents think?'

'About the name?'

'About you and her.'

'They know she likes me. They want her to be happy.'

'But you told me before, she's not a Nayak.'

'No, she's Vaisya. Merchant caste. But her parents, they are good people. They want that she is happy. From their side, they said they would let me marry her… before this all happened.'

210

'And now?' I ask, as we set off again.

'Now I don't know. She doesn't want to stop seeing me.' He falls silent for a while, as if deciding how much more he should tell me, then he plunges abruptly into another aspect of the affair: 'It's not like maybe you're thinking. It's very pure. No... sexual relations. Just we hold hands. And we talk. But come...' He stops beside a dark, narrow doorway. 'In a moment you can meet her.'

Eleven

We climb several flights of stairs. The building is divided into flats, none of them large enough for the occupants' needs, so most of their lives spill untidily onto the stairwell through open doors. Prithi's home is on the top floor and, untypically, her door is closed, so we knock and wait, while two sets of neighbours size me up. Then the door is opened by a fine-featured girl who, with eyes cast demurely downwards, stands aside to let us in. Mohamd pecks her on the cheek, as she proffers me a shy handshake. She wears a graceful, silk, ankle-length skirt, with a matching, tight-waisted blouse. Her head is bare, with the hair tied back in an elegant knot, revealing delicate silver earrings. She makes both of us look shabby.

Inside the small apartment, a middle-aged man sits slumped on a white plastic chair in front of a large, old-fashioned television, an empty glass tumbler at his ankles. Without taking his eyes off the screen, he stretches out a hand and gives a welcoming grunt. Then, spotting the whisky bottle, he quickly hauls himself to his feet to find two extra glasses, thereby revealing the single white chair to be a stack of three, so Mohamd issues one of these for each of us. Prithi stands politely near the door, while the father fills his own glass and half-fills Mohamd's. He is about to do the same for me, but Mohamd stops him.

'You prefer beer,' he says. 'Outside I can buy.'

'Whisky's fine,' I protest, but Mohamd has already gone.

'My father speaks no English,' says Prithi, smiling sweetly.

'We've invited a neighbour, who does. He comes from Kerala and Mumda said you made holiday there…' She dries up, uncertain what to say next. Her English seems remarkably good, but she is unaccustomed to the hostess role. In desperation, she makes a big show of remembering something and slips away to a small curtained alcove – presumably the kitchen – leaving me alone with Dad, who has all but drained his glass. He gives me a second chance to refuse, before topping himself up, with a 'might-as-well-knock-this-back-while-you-wait-for-your-beer' kind of gesture. Then, uncertain how else to entertain me, he reverts to the TV sitcom, chuckling loudly at successive inanities, before courteously explaining each of them in Hindi.

'Sorry for late,' says Mohamd, when at last he reappears. 'I met one friend. Number three Spanish guide. We have small business problem. I tell you later.' Meanwhile Prithi has emerged with the remembered item, a large bowl of crisps, and the ensuing quarter of an hour is taken up with one or other of them pressing me to take another handful. 'Is OK for you we finish these, take dinner later?' asks Mohamd. 'Only, mostly it is Salu's mother who is cooking. Salu not so quick.'

'It's fine,' I tell him, calculating that I'd have been well through my main course at Gajendra's by now. Then Prithi says she'll go to boil some water for the rice.

'What do you think?' whispers Mohamd, as she disappears behind the curtain. 'Is she all right?'

'I think she's lovely,' I tell him sincerely, but wondering anxiously where the relationship can lead. 'She seems very well educated. Does she have a job?'

'She's still at school. Final year. She want to study computers, but her mother say she should marry. I think this is why she go to Udaipur, to find husband.'

I hadn't realised that Prithi was so young. She looks so polished.

Yet she can't have been more than thirteen when I first saw her on the rooftop; younger than Mohamd's wife even. And he's been in love with her for all these years, waiting patiently, chastely, for something that cannot now happen.

A knock at the door announces the Keralan light relief and a middle-aged man shuffles in. He's wearing the typical South Indian ankle-length *lungi* tied round his waist and, in classic Keralan fashion, hitches up the bottom to make a knee-length wrap, while Mohamd pours his whisky; then he sits expectantly facing me, waiting to be amused.

'So, you're from Kerala?'

'Yes.'

Pause.

Mohamd tiptoes towards the alcove.

'I went there last year. I went to Cochin and Periyar and a beach resort…'

'Oh.'

Another pause, in which Mohamd slips behind the curtain and Prithi's father starts snoring.

'Very different from Rajasthan,' I offer, hoping to draw my audience out.

'Very different,' he agrees.

'You must miss it.'

A long silence, while he thinks, before stating his considered position: 'Not so much.'

'How long have you lived in Rajasthan?' I ask, trying to drive the note of panic from my voice.

An even longer silence, broken by muted girlish giggles from behind the curtain.

'One year,' he says at last.

The conversation, if such it can be called, limps on in this fashion for what seems like an hour, until Mohamd returns to check on glasses. 'You don't mind?' he enquires, with a nod towards the curtain. 'I think you have plenty to talk about. Just ten more minutes.' He vanishes again and noises off suggest rather more cuddling than cooking, as the ten minutes stretch to twenty and ever more ludicrous lines of enquiry are opened up. My Keralan counterpart seems wholly at ease with the cavernous silences, smiling benignly in anticipation of my next far-fetched question; but he never spares me more than three or four syllables in reply, never feeds me any cue that would let me do the answering. I'm seconds away from feigning a life-threatening illness, when the curtain twitches aside and Prithi's dinner is served.

'How many books you write?' asked the hair-combing boy, munching breakfast chapatis on the neighbouring rooftop.

'Two,' I called down to him.

'Only two? How many years old you are?' He plainly found my lifetime's output to be less than prolific.

'I've only been writing for four or five years,' I answered defensively. 'I used to be a lawyer.'

'I know this job,' said my inquisitor approvingly. 'This good money job.'

'I suppose so, yes.'

'How many books you sell?'

'I don't know exactly. Twenty thousand, perhaps…'

'This not so good money job.'

'It's a different kind of satisfaction…'

'You are famous?' he pressed, with a mystified frown.

'As a writer?' I laughed, amused at his dogged interview technique. 'Not really…'

'As lawyer?'

'Maybe a little, years ago…'

'Why you not get new lawyer job? Good success job? Mumda say you very wise man,' he added, as if to say, we all make misjudgements. 'Now I go work in shop.' The conversation closed as abruptly as it began, leaving me nursing my tattered self respect.

'Still no en suite tomorrow night,' said Manu, bringing my breakfast. 'But don't worry. I think of something.' He gave a conspiratorial wink and slipped away, leaving me listening to the musician boys' songs drifting up over the ramparts.

'Sorry for disturb,' said the warm voice of Narayan, unexpectedly appearing at my table. 'Mumda called, sir, asked me to wait with you, while he little bit late.' Deferentially, he made to join me. 'I think you like this Rajasthani music, sir. Also from my side, very much I like. At my home, there is CD, sir, very same.'

'You really don't have to call me "sir", Narayan.'

'Show respect to win respect,' he answered and I decided not to press the point. 'You sleep well, sir?'

'Fine, thanks,' I lied. The truth was, I'd hardly slept at all. I could keep it all at bay during the day. Swept along by the close, supportive fellowship all around me, I could push the darker concerns to the back of my mind; but the nights were filled with blank desolation: despair for Mohamd, mixed with impotent failure. 'But tell me,' I asked, falsely bright. 'Those songs the boys are singing – are they modern or traditional?'

'Traditional, sir.'

'And what are they about?'

'Oh, different things. Mostly boy and girl in village who love each other, but cannot marry because of different caste.'

'The usual,' I laughed. 'And what about you? Have your parents chosen *your* wife?'

'Not yet. I am twenty-two. Normally in our society, the boy is married by twenty-four, but I don't have good job. My father say, definitely I must be engaged this year. We are Shudra, sir – farming caste – but my father work as salesman, always travelling, so not much time.'

'And how do you feel about it?' I had sensed a lack of enthusiasm.

'I have English girlfriend, sir... From Yorkshire... You know Skipton?' He looked shyly at his feet, the shyness accentuating his handsomeness, and I imagined the combination working wonders in the Dales. 'Few weeks before, she come to Jaisalmer, take camel safari. I give her your email address, sir. I hope you don't mind. She tell me she write you, because Mumda say you very wise man. She want to know what you think. About her and me. We both want to know, sir.'

I laughed nervously, feeling underequipped for a morning of marriage guidance. 'We can talk when we go to the desert...'

'As you like, sir. Camels all arranged and already I am planning special... I don't say this word so well... special itinererary.' He stood to check for signs of our friend in the square.

'You look for Mumda?' asked a passing waiter. 'Right now downside with Manu.'

'I didn't want to rush your breakfast,' Mohamd explained, rising sleepily to his feet. 'But I've spoken to my father-in-law. Tomorrow we see my wife.'

'But that's our camel day.' I looked to Narayan for support and there followed a lengthy debate in their own language.

'You can take the camels to her village,' said Mohamd eventually. 'All the normal tourist sites you have seen, but this will be something new. Then later I can meet you there by motorbike.'

'Well, as long as we're back by dinner time. Alex is worse than me when it comes to punctuality! Which reminds me... I really don't think you should come with me to Jodhpur.'

'It's my duty. You've come so far.'

'You need to be on form for their camel safari. And you need to be on time. You won't be either, if you've been up all night, driving home.'

'It's no problem…'

'*Please*, Mohamd. I've told them so much about you…'

His telephone saved him from further entreaties. It was Gajendra, inviting me to his home. He said he couldn't be there himself, but his mother and wife were expecting me and Mohamd seized eagerly on the distraction, summoning Tanu with another motorbike to give Narayan a lift. Then an amiable young giant known as Chief, with a bigger, more powerful machine to match his bulk, tagged along, so it is quite a cavalcade that presents itself at Gajendra's home.

The single-storied house is smaller, plainer, more box-like than I expected and, like the other dwellings here on the edge of the city, stands in bare sandy earth, indistinguishable from the surrounding desert. Yet by Jaisalmer standards, this is doubtless a fashionable suburb. 'Goppu build this,' says Mohamd, vicariously proud. 'His father no big salary.'

There are two front doors side by side and the house is divided in half – one for Gajendra, his wife and daughter, the other for his parents. A family group is waiting on the steps: a stout, middle-aged woman, holding a pretty, olive-skinned child; beside them, an elegant waif of a wife, with a garland of marigolds to hang round my neck. 'I should have brought presents,' I whisper, but Mohamd sweeps this aside and the five of us surge into Gajendra's half of the house, effectively a single room, dominated by a big double bed. Taking the baby from its grandmother, Mohamd makes straight for the bed and gestures to me to join him, as platters of food are pressed on us.

'Take, eat,' urge Tanu and Chief, apparently feeling that I must sample everything before they can tuck in. However, Mohamd's mobile is ringing.

'It's for you,' he says wryly.

'Good day, sir. How are you? I am very fine, thank you...' Tanu and Chief exchange hungry glances, wondering how far the social niceties need prevail. 'I hope my wife is looking after you. Also that you have time to see my marriage photos... But sorry, sir, already I must go.'

Mohamd has remembered that he must go too. 'To fetch one diamond necklace, for Ravi tonight,' he explains, handing the baby to Narayan. 'Jeweller friend, he is lending...' So the burden of entertaining me falls on the photograph album.

Much of the material is familiar from Mohamd's portfolio, but there are two whole series that are new: two marriages – one the joyful union of a postmaster's son with a radiant Brahmin bride, the other the reluctant joining together of two stone-breaking, camel-breeding... who knows? I never did find out... maybe marriage-broking Bhils. And the contrast is heart-breaking.

Maybe sensing this, Narayan tells me something I never knew: 'Mohamd, I think maybe you know this, he is Gajendra's best friend. He is many people's best friend. But always, from first days, doing the guiding, taking tourists to Riyaz's shop, in everything Mumda and Goppu they are... I don't know the word...'

'Inseparable?'

'Yes, inseparable. But Goppu's family, they know very well Mumda's condition. They say, you cannot bring that boy to our home. Some of his uncles, still they say this. But Goppu – you know this also, sir – he is strong. To his father and mother he say, this one friend, this Mohamd, for me he is like my brother. If you send him away, you send me away. I respect you in everything, I do everything you want of me, but not this. And today – well, already you have seen it, sir – even the baby Mumda is holding.'

It's Narayan's longest ever speech, and his most impassioned, shedding new light on the photo that fell from the back of

Mohamd's album, but so prominently displayed in Gajendra's. It shows two indivisible friends, each with an arm hugging tightly the other's shoulder: a small triumph over centuries of separation.

'Kuldhara you have seen,' Mohamd admits. 'But musician, no...'

The player at the gateway looks old enough to be my grandfather: shrivelled, skeletal and stooping, almost crushed by the weight of a cast-off military jacket, worn over dirty white shepherd's apparel; but his playing is remarkable. He plays two separate oboe-like pipes simultaneously: one, using conventional woodwind fingering and breathing, supplies the melody; the other, a constant, harmonised drone, like the plangent wail of a bagpipe, except that here there's no bag. Even as the player sucks in breath to power the first pipe, some complex pumping of his wizened cheeks sends a steady stream of air down the second and the drone never falters.

'It's time we talked,' I whisper, as the pipes play on.

'You remember when first you came to Jaisalmer?' Mohamd nods pensively to the melancholy beat. 'Slow music, sad music, then I did not like...' Now it plainly suits his mood, but we are running out of time.

'We need to talk,' I insist and reluctantly he refocuses, giving some kind of instruction to Narayan, Tanu and Chief, who leave for the dried-up river bed.

'Looking for fossils,' Mohamd explains and the musician, losing most of his audience, decides to finish the performance. Mohamd passes him some folded banknotes and the two of us are alone.

'You said you had a business problem,' I prompt. 'You and the third Spanish guide.'

'Tanu also,' Mohamd answers. 'All three Spanish guides. We are like partners. Three musketeers. All for one, one for all. Six months before, Akram – this is number three guide – he meet big Spanish businessman, who need help making imports here in Rajasthan, so all three, we help him find contacts, pay money to right peoples… But now this man, he have all their names, he just go to them direct.'

'What about the money you paid?'

'Many times we telephone, also write, but no answer.'

'How much have you lost?'

'Three *lakh* rupees.'

'That's three hundred thousand, isn't it?'

Mohamd nods grimly. 'All this Akram have paid but, like I told you, three musketeers…' Doubtless, his own third share would pay for most of the outstanding building work on his house. 'It's OK,' he assures me. 'Ten thousand already I give to Akram. Rest I can borrow. Just for few months. With Italian movie money, soon I pay back. Same other small loans, even your money for Spanish lessons.'

'There's no need. Finishing your house is more important…'

'No, definitely I pay. Then maybe you still buy me air ticket.'

I smile, giving in. 'But what if the film project doesn't happen?'

'I have two big groups booked with top Spanish tour company.'

'They must think highly of you.'

'Number One in all North India, they say. Except for two. These are owner's brothers, so always they get best jobs. But yes, they think highly.' He hesitates briefly, then presses on. 'You know, since I start my guiding work, all six, seven years, I get only two complaints. One from American client, completely mad, complain about everything.' He pauses again, reluctant to continue.

'And the other?'

'It was you.'

Twelve

'You said I was late,' Mohamd reminds me. 'For that camel safari.' I start to apologise, but he cuts me short. 'You were right. I had to learn.' He looks up, relieved to see Narayan and the others coming back, bearing one fossil each, none bigger than a pea. 'Tonight for sure we can talk,' he promises.

'Sir, Chief is love-sick,' laughs Tanu, as Chief squirms bashfully, not naturally the confiding type. He does, however, reluctantly explain. His family is wealthy, one of the richest in Jaisalmer, with a substantial house on the outskirts of the city, near the luxury hotels. He drives his own car, as well as the motorbike. Yet his parents, like Narayan's, are strictly speaking farmers. Their money came from advantageous land deals – perhaps to the luxury hoteliers (he doesn't say) – but now they aspire for him to marry well, cement their fortunes with a strategic alliance: applications from minor princesses considered, a well-to-do merchant's daughter at the very least. Meanwhile, he's secretly in love with a humble Shudra girl from his own caste.

'Certainly a variation on a theme,' I sigh, as he waits expectantly for the patent remedy that I fail to deliver.

'Tanu also love-sick,' chuckles Chief, getting his own back. 'Spanish tourist girl, every day writing. Face like a lorry driver...' Tanu punches him hard on his burly broad shoulder. 'His parents found her photo, tell him no more write letters. They want an untouchable for a daughter-in-law, not a trucker!'

'You see?' Narayan smiles wryly, as Tanu lands further

ineffectual blows. 'None of us are free. That's why we're all friends. All same bloody problem!'

'You should write one more book,' says Mohamd, standing apart from the general merriment. 'Tell people all what happen here. Make them understand.'

'Does Ravi's father own the whole *haveli*?' I asked, standing back to admire the flashing lights.

'Only the shop and small flat,' said Narayan, looking after me, while Mohamd ticked off another wedding invitation. 'Careful, sir!' I'd been about to walk backwards into a pair of opulently saddled white horses tethered near the doorway. 'Ravi's older brother marry also,' he explained, as a tide of people swept us up some stairs, while a few dozen others pushed downwards. 'Brides, two sisters from other side of city.'

Halfway up the stairs, we saw the two brothers, having their turbans tied amidst a dense circle of well wishers. The rooftop, by contrast, was almost deserted. Apart from some over-excited children, just one well-dressed couple sat stiffly to one side. They did nothing to acknowledge us, but their mixture of boredom and aloofness told me they were there out of duty.

'Ravi's landlord,' whispered Narayan. 'Rich Brahmins…'
'And Ravi?'
'Vaisya, sir. Merchant caste. Also not so rich.'
'You wouldn't think so from the number of guests,' I laughed, as a crowd, spilling onto the roof, thrust two bashful bridegrooms into the fresh evening air.

'So much of honour, sir,' said Ravi, shaking my hand.
Behind the borrowed diamond necklace, he was every bit as baby-faced as he had been five years ago, but at least he had scrubbed most of the betel juice from his teeth. He called to Pratap, his equally boyish elder brother, anxious to boast of his

Western guest and the two of them stood goofily before me, looking like under-rehearsed pageboys from someone else's wedding. Then an uncle came to steer them down towards the horses: they were about to be made men.

In the street, several hundred guests compete for space with a throng of tourists, drawn by the lights and the noise. A discordant band strikes up to lead us to the brides' homes and the first sighting by the grooms of their long-term destinies. A hand-drawn cart bears trumpet-like loudspeakers to reinforce the musicians' ear-splitting efforts and the procession sets off behind it: Pratap first, Ravi second, followed by the men of the family, then the women, with a dozen ragged street urchins, bearing battery-powered neon strip lights, scampering alongside to light our way.

'That's how I earned money,' says Mohamd, appearing at my side. 'When I first came to Jaisalmer.'

'Better than selling fossils?' I ask, but he doesn't hear me. He is too busy resisting the concerted effort of his friends to persuade him to join in the dancing. Narayan is already working up a sweat at the heart of a tight circle of Jaisalmer manhood, interposed between the musicians and the horses. Chief and Tanu jig more clumsily on the fringes. Even Gajendra, casting dignity to the winds, is punching the air with the best of them. Only Riyaz, incongruous in blazer and tie, stands watching from a distance, plucking up the missing courage to let go.

'Please, sir, please,' cries an unkempt boy, barely fourteen years old, pulling impatiently at my sleeve. I shake my head, embarrassed, and he turns his attentions to Mohamd, dragging him closer to the fray. While my friend shuffles uncomfortably on the spot, merely shifting his weight from foot to foot, the boy performs a hip-wiggling, pelvis-thrusting repertory of steps drawn from Bollywood. Like the other young men in the melée, he's making do. The girls are all at the back of the procession.

Dropping back to check on morale amongst the female contingent, I find them having a much duller time. No dancing. No exuberance of any kind. Just a bit of child-minding, a lot of gossip and some periodic bursts of dirge-like singing. A firecracker landing near their feet sparks the sole sign of liveliness.

'Hey, Patrick!' calls a stranger, running down from the head of the parade to take my hand and drag me back towards the dance group. 'Mohamd sent me to find you!' he bellows in my ear, as I struggle to imitate the prevailing dance style. He is easily the most presentable of Mohamd's friends: tall and slim, sporting a crimson open-necked shirt and tightly cut black suit to good effect. He has fair, unblemished skin and dark, thoughtful eyes, set beneath dense black curls. But it's the smile that would get any but the grouchiest curmudgeon onto the dance floor. 'My name is Akram,' he shouts, dancing ever more frenetically to dispel my inhibitions.

'Number three Spanish guide?' I holler back and he nods, looking modestly pleased that I've heard of him.

And of course! It was Akram, the good-looking boy on the Himalayan holiday. It was Akram, the handsome youth in the square, to whom Mohamd gave the bundle of cash. Akram, my unlikely partner on the dance floor.

'Come to dinner tomorrow night,' I yell impulsively. 'I'd like some friends of mine to meet you.'

'Why you friend of Mumda?' asks the rooftop ten-year-old, chewing his morning chapati.

'We met when he was my guide,' I begin.

'I know. I told you, I know everything. You meet here in Jaisalmer when Mumda still student. Already you old then, like Mumda father…'

'I thought he was talented,' I try to explain, but the boy looks blank. 'Clever,' I try again.

'I am clever,' says the boy. 'Mumda not so clever.'

'I wanted to try to help him,' I continue, ignoring the boast. 'Help him get a better job.'

'Mumda still guide,' says the boy bluntly.

'Well, yes, but these days a different sort of guide. Now he takes tourists all over India.'

'Your help do this?' asks the boy, moving from breakfast to hair-combing.

'Not really,' I admit, filled with shame at how little I have ever done for him. 'I did pay for some training…' The boy looks blank again. 'Like school,' I suggest. 'Only for guides.'

'Mumda learn everything from Manu,' says the boy, dismissing my input. 'You have many young friend?'

'Not many.' I try to take the focus off myself by asking my interrogator whether he goes to school, but he's having none of it.

'Why Mumda?' he challenges.

I hesitate. I have had this conversation before, with so many English friends. I have tried to explain how it never really felt like a choice. An accident of timing seemed to choose Mohamd for me. 'He was lucky,' I tell the boy. 'The right place at the right time.'

'You help other Indian boy?' He puts the question neutrally, but it would be only natural for him to hope.

'Just Mumda,' I tell him firmly.

'I have friend in London,' says the boy, reasserting his self-sufficiency. 'He send me photo, tell me one day I come to England. Now I go work in shop.'

I turn to find Manu watching affectionately. 'Like Mumda, when he first came to city,' he chuckles nostalgically, then returns to the present. 'Good news!' he says excitedly. 'En suite room! You remember young couple next door to you? Tonight they sleep in desert, taking tent and camelman to cook… I tell them, everyone who come to Jaisalmer must do this,' he adds with a roguish wink.

★

'That's her village?' I ask, amazed.

It looks like a battle zone. Chaotic mounds of rubble lie everywhere, with piles of larger boulders suggesting the stone-breakers bring their work home with them. Most of the buildings look half-ruined, though they are, I suspect, merely half-built, waiting for extra cash that never quite materialises. None is taller than a single storey, few more ambitious than a single room; and there are no discernible streets, merely haphazard gaps between the debris.

We are early. Narayan arranged to meet Mohamd here at twelve, but that's almost half an hour away. We tie the camels to a withered tree and continue on foot, as a teenage boy ambles out to meet us. 'Mumda's brother-in-law,' explains Narayan. 'He says sorry, no English.'

We follow the boy through the desolate landscape to a stone-walled enclosure, surrounding two small, more or less finished buildings. From the first of these comes a tall, firmly veiled woman, pursuing the domestic chores, as if we were invisible. 'Mumda's mother-in-law,' says Narayan. 'Never once he will see her face. Not till day she die.' Without glancing in our direction, she hands two glasses of goaty *chai* to her son, who wordlessly gestures that we might prefer to savour them in the second, smaller building. We follow him inside, scarcely able to stand up straight, while he clears blankets from a *charpai* so that we can sit and brings a chipped formica coffee table and a plastic garden chair from a neighbour's to fill more of the restricted space. Then he stations himself near the door, smiling amiably as he watches our awkward silence.

A shorter, plumper woman passes the open doorway. She too is veiled and angles her gaze inflexibly away from us. 'That's her,' says Narayan. I half-rise to greet her, but he restrains me and we lapse again into silence, still watched by the brother-in-law.

'I brought you this,' says Narayan eventually, taking a small square parcel, wrapped in newspaper, from his jacket pocket. 'My CD of that singer-boy, sir. Later I get one more.'

'But they said in the market, it's not available…'

'Always I can hear the boy near the gate,' he insists, pressing the CD into my hands.

'Thanks, it'll bring back memories.'

'Not all of them good, I think.' He pauses for longer than I'd have wished, leaving too much time to evaluate the truth of this. Then, unexpectedly, he reaches out to place a comforting hand on my knee. 'Don't upset yourself, sir. Mumda's friends will help him.'

I was managing fine until then – keeping a well-controlled balance between the joyous comradeship of my days and the lonely, sleepless sadness of the nights – but that simple empathetic gesture threatens to unleash everything I've been holding back. 'Can we go for a walk?' I ask, getting briskly to my feet.

'I have telephone this morning,' says Narayan outside. 'From Yorkshire, sir. My girlfriend ask me, what did Mr Patrick say?'

I hesitate. Whatever I say will be given infallible, *ex cathedra* status. 'How long was your girlfriend here?' I ask him in the end.

'In India, sir? Maybe six weeks, in Jaisalmer almost one…'

'I think she needs to come back.'

'To know me better, you mean?'

'To know the country you come from. She'll never understand you, if she doesn't. You might have a different attitude to servants!' I laugh.

'Servants?' He looks mystified.

'Just a joke. What I meant was, it's never easy stepping outside your culture.'

'Thank you, sir,' he says admiringly. 'We didn't think like this. So much you know, sir.' I shrug, uncomfortable to find such sage-like significance attributed to an off-the-cuff thought. 'Was it easy, sir? Switching from lawyering to writing?'

'Easier than I thought,' I answer, wondering why he wants to know. 'The biggest change was sitting all on my own, with just a desk and a computer...' I break off, sensing that Narayan's mind is elsewhere.

'Do you think it would be easy for me, sir? Switching from Jaisalmer to Yorkshire?'

'Oh, I see... Well, harder than I used to think. But I'm sure you'll make it work...'

We are outside the village, near the camels, which are feeding on the bedraggled remains of some prickly acacia trees. I ask him about a nearby cactus-like plant, covered in lilac-coloured flowers, the only thing of beauty in the whole of this miserable landscape. 'It's poisonous,' Narayan says bluntly. 'It makes you go blind.' I take this as our cue to return to the waiting room, where we continue to wait.

I decide to broach something riskier: 'You know about Prithi, I think?' Narayan nods, looking embarrassed. 'Mohamd says he might have married her, if he wasn't already...' Narayan uneasily glances towards the young woman outside. 'I don't know how these things work in India,' I fumble onwards. 'But just supposing... I mean, I don't know if it's even possible...'

'You mean, could he *divorce* her?' asks Narayan quietly, as if afraid that someone might hear and understand the forbidden word.

'I'm just exploring whether it's an option, before things get more complicated... I mean, they're complicated now, but at least they don't have children.'

Narayan looks even more uncomfortable. 'I think, sir, maybe

229

ten times worse than if he first said "no" to this marriage. Not just for him, but whole family. Forever outside society.'

Which seems to put an end to that line of enquiry.

Narayan looks again at his watch. It is almost three-fifteen. 'I could go back outside, try my mobile,' he suggests, setting off on what I know is a hopeless quest, but I'm relieved that he doesn't hurry back. I like him a lot. I like his solid strength; I like the depth of sympathy behind the rugged exterior. But the strain of making small-talk is worse than sitting here alone.

Time passes slowly. I draw patterns with my shoes on the bare earth floor. I study every tiny detail of a poster for last year's Desert Festival on the wall. If the instructions on a tin of axel grease had been in English, I'd have started reading them, learnt them by heart even. At least the brother-in-law is no longer doing sentry duty.

From time to time, the two women pass the doorway. I look longingly for evidence of anything resembling cooking activity, but they are both pottering aimlessly. Then I notice something more important. Mohamd's wife has stopped to confer with her mother. She is standing in profile, bolt upright with a water pot on her head, sharply silhouetted against the light and, slowly, it dawns on me that she is not simply plump. She is several months pregnant.

Thirteen

'You are hungry, I think, sir.' Narayan stoops to re-enter our tiny shared cell. It is close to four o'clock, and still no prospect of nutrition. 'They wait for Mumda,' he apologises.

'Something must have gone wrong,' I fret. 'We ought to go back, try to find him. There's only just enough daylight...' But suddenly there's a crunch of wheels on rubble. Mohamd has come in Chief's car. So have Tanu and a couple of unknown comrades in dark glasses. They pile out of the car, looking like gangsters. Except for Mohamd. A turquoise kaftan and spotless white trousers have supplanted the tweedy jacket. Even his hair has been tied in a pony tail.

'Sorry for late,' he says warily. 'We waited for Goppu, but today so much shopping his clients want to do. Every half hour he promise, just ten minutes more. Finally we have to come without him, by car for more quick.' He pauses, sensing that none of this is going down very well. 'So how are you?' he asks apprehensively.

'A bit tired.'

'Tired of camel?'

'Tired of waiting,' I tell him, trying not to sound as angry as I feel.

'Tired of everything?' he asks, in a lifeless tone that tells me more about his own state of mind than any imagined despondency of mine.

I make a clumsy attempt at reassurance: 'It's just... I don't

231

know… Some things might have gone better.' He manages a half-smile, nodding sadly and I try to sound more believably forgiving. 'But none of it matters. Only that it will soon be dark.'

'Can you stay for twenty minutes?' He too is fighting hard to sound positive. 'Just to see my wife. Also, you are hungry, I think. Very fast they make food. Then you come back by car. Narayan take camels.'

I acquiesce and follow Mohamd back into the claustrophobic cubicle. 'You didn't tell me she was pregnant,' I whisper, as if there were anyone to hear and understand. He nods distractedly, but his thoughts seem far away. 'Doesn't that change things?' I press him. 'Surely you have to make the child your priority now, give it a future.'

He forces a defeated smile of agreement, as the brother-in-law brings the wife, almost thrusting her in through the doorway. She pauses just inside, taking stock behind her veil of the place where I am sitting, then darts like a frightened animal to the opposite corner of the room, forcing her face into the right-angle made by the walls. Mohamd approaches her, talking softly, putting an arm around her, coaxing, pleading, half-compelling her to turn round. Unwillingly, she revolves, manoeuvred a couple of paces forward by her husband's forceful grip, while slowly, with his other hand, he reaches for the veil, still mouthing gentle words of encouragement. Suddenly she understands and flinches, struggles, jerks her head away. For just a fraction of a second, I glimpse her anguished face, screwed up tightly in shame. Then she pulls the veil back down again and runs to bury her face in the corner.

'Now do you understand?' asks Mohamd after a silence. 'Now do you see why I'm unhappy?'

'You're late!' cried Alex, with a note of triumph.

I had sprinted up the Killa Bhawan stairs, scarcely dry from my shower, but it was no use arguing that I was spot on time. I should have remembered: Alex always arrives early and considers it outrageous whenever other people fail to do the same.

Fortunately Akram was even earlier. 'We've been well looked after,' purred Elektra, transparently content to pass any amount of time in the young man's company. 'But what a place!' she enthused, with a wave towards the view.

'You insisted on somewhere more expensive for us,' grumbled Alex. 'Never take his advice, Akram. It'll cost you a fortune!' Akram smiled insecurely, still feeling his way, then asked them about their tour. 'Too much shopping,' said Alex. 'My wife, you have to understand, is a perfect illustration of a capitalist economy overheating, whereas all that I desire is an honest tailor to make me some shirts. But not at the price I paid in Jaipur!'

'He paid four pounds,' Elektra intervened. 'In London it costs him nearly that, just to have a shirt laundered!'

Akram laughed with incredulity. 'He could buy them here, wear them once and throw them away...'

'A decent wife would wash and iron them for me, don't you think, Akram?'

'My wife would do mine,' he answered, growing more confident.

'I'm not *entirely* certain about that,' said Elektra, fixing him with her fiercest consulting room stare, but he rose to the moment.

'Of course she would,' he retorted. 'I'd say to her, "Darling, if you love me, you must do this." ' And he bathed us all in a version of the smile that he'd turn on the wife.

'If he says it like that, she'll do anything,' whispered Elektra, while Alex, laughing heartily at the skilled young manager of women, tried to press a beer on him.

'Thank you, no. I drink always only Pepsi,' he excused himself.

'You're Muslim, surely?' asked Elektra.

'How did you know?' asked Akram, as if fearing what further secrets the psychotherapist might have penetrated.

'Your name.' She laid a reassuring hand on his forearm, letting it linger there a moment. 'Not a total giveaway like "Mohamd", but all the same…'

'Oh, but you're wrong,' he responded playfully, looking to me to tell the 'Muslim name, Hindu boy' story.

I made it last as long as possible, in the hope that the character in question might appear before its end; but then Alex ran out of patience and we set off without him in a pair of autorickshaws, which Akram commandeered with brisk efficiency.

'He's terrific,' says Alex, as always a man of quick judgements. 'But should I trust him with my wife, I ask myself? A more suspicious man might wonder why it is that Elektra thought I'd wish to share a taxi with you!' Alex is clearly enjoying his holiday.

He is even more delighted with Gajendra, the budding businessman, who joins us at our table in The Jaisal Treat. In fact, so detailed is Alex's interest in the young man's business plans that I half expect him to buy a stake in the restaurant. 'Sensational!' he enthuses. 'And this is the guy you've booked as tomorrow's guide? You're really spoiling us!'

Then in drifts Mohamd.

I'm not sure how many marriages he has attended since last I saw him, but they have clearly taken their toll. His eyes look glazed, his speech is slurred and his once immaculate kaftan bears the stains of various buffets. 'Zzzorryforlate,' he mumbles, addressing no one in particular.

'This is Mohamd,' I reluctantly admit.

Elektra raises a disbelieving eyebrow, while Alex looks stony-faced. Even Gajendra seems momentarily dumb-struck, but Akram rises smartly to his feet – not to steer the new arrival away, as I find myself hoping – rather to surrender the seat between Alex and myself and move to the end of the table. Mohamd, grinning vacuously, takes the empty chair.

I have never seen Alex so strikingly lost for words and it falls to Elektra to extend the preliminary courtesies. However, she has hardly more than asked after Mohamd's day, when a total stranger – a dishevelled, unshaven mute of indeterminate age – plonks himself unannounced between Akram and me. He presumably arrived with Mohamd. Mohamd must indeed have issued an invitation, yet no one – least of all Mohamd – explains his presence. Akram simply ignores him, much as Alex and Elektra now ignore Mohamd, turning all of their attention on Gajendra. This leaves me with Mohamd, quietly snoring on one side of me, and the silent stranger, cleaning his nails with the point of a fork, on the other. Thank goodness for Akram at the head of the table.

'A bit of a character,' he whispers, meaning Alex, while I ponder who it is that he reminds me of: something in the warm, open smile…

'There's only one Alex,' I laugh. Then a thought strikes me. 'You're not free on Monday? For their camel safari? Mohamd's meant to be doing it, but I'd feel happier if you could go instead.'

'We could both do it,' he offers, loath to cut his friend out.

'Alex is a hard man to please.'

'Trust me,' says Akram, shaking my hand, and instinctively I feel that I can. Yet I only met him last night.

'So why did Mohamd keep you hidden all this time?' I ask, as the first of the food arrives. 'Have you known each other long?'

'A third of my life,' laughs Akram. 'Since I was twelve.'

'You're only eighteen?'

'Last month,' he confesses, smiling modestly. 'Mumda like a second father to me,' he says, looking fondly at his somnolent mentor. Then, suddenly more expansive, he tells me how he hadn't always planned to be a guide. His real ambition was the police force. He understood, of course, that he'd have to bribe his way in and duly went along to the interview, armed with two hundred thousand rupees – a major stretch for his family, but they felt they could treat it as an investment. Once he was in, there would be plenty of bribes flowing back. But the recruiting officers demanded five hundred thousand, which was out of the question, so he turned to Mohamd.

'Hey, you down there, a toast!' proposes Alex – always a sure sign that he's on a high. 'To Gajendra and a nation-wide chain of Jaisal Treats!'

'And to Akram!' adds Elektra, with a wink.

'To them both,' I answer whole-heartedly.

No one mentions Mohamd or the mysterious mute.

'May I serve him something?' asks Akram, meaning the stranger, the only one with an empty plate.

'Who is he?' I ask, unaccustomed to gate-crashers at my dinner parties.

'I don't know. Mohamd has many friends.' He gives an embarrassed smile, then points again to the food. 'I think we have enough.'

His generosity emboldens me to seek another favour: 'Akram, I've no right to ask this, but let me explain... I've done little enough for Mohamd. So much less than I intended. He'll probably say it's none of my business, but I've made up my mind, I'm going to talk to him in the morning, before I leave for Jodhpur. When he's... you know, when he's better. I'm going to tell him that he's got to change. For the sake of his family. For his own sake. He needs to see less of his drinking pals, spend more of his time with his Muslim friends – you and Riyaz. It's his only hope. But first I need to know... Will you *be there* for him?' Akram promises. 'And will you write to me? Send me emails? Let me know how he is?' Akram promises again.

'After all he do for me,' he says simply.

'Listen,' says Alex, suddenly tugging at my sleeve. He has seen it all in a flash: 'Gajendra's the one you ought to be supporting,' he whispers confidentially, brooking no debate. 'Wish my son showed half as much enterprise! Switch horses while you can.' He glances dismissively towards the comatose figure between us. 'Anyway, Gajendra's much more your sort.'

'Alex, you don't understand...'

'You're right,' he interrupts, suddenly wholly serious. 'I don't understand. I remember how you used to talk about Mohamd, how exceptional you said he was, how full of promise. I can't relate any of that to what I'm seeing tonight. What's happened in between?'

'He got married.'

'Ah, now that I do understand!' cries Alex, back in jocular mood and hoping Elektra will overhear. She is, however, busy with Akram.

'I mean, you don't understand about "switching". It's not like that. 'It's not a matter of who's "more my sort". I'm *committed*. I can't change now, any more than you can swap your children for someone else's that impress you more.'

'I never speak to my children,' says Alex emphatically. 'They're all failures.'

'The reason you favour Gajendra is because he's like you – an achiever, a success story. But that's the point. Gajendra doesn't *need* help. Mohamd does. In some ways, more now than ever.'

'He should pull himself together... Like most of my esteemed wife's clients,' he adds pointedly, but Elektra is still otherwise distracted. Then a new thought puts a mischievous smile on his face. 'You know that he's hopelessly in debt?' Alex is plainly gearing up to tell me something that I'll be unhappy to hear. 'Forever taking new loans to pay the interest on the old ones?'

'Gajendra did give me an inkling, yes.'

'Well, he's just been telling me where a lot of the money goes.' He pauses looking pleased with himself, letting my mind fill with lurid possibilities.

'He's got a large extended family,' I try to explain. 'A lot of hangers on…'

'Buying friendship,' Alex cuts in brutally. 'Helping people he can't afford to help and hoping to be loved for it. Ask Gajendra.'

'I can't believe that's how Gajendra put it,' I protest, but Alex simply shrugs in a 'suit yourself' manner.

'Like that politician they locked up for buying votes,' he persists, taking pleasure in twisting the knife. 'If it's any consolation, Gajendra did say he'll stick by him, but then nobody's perfect!'

Elektra, never one to waste time, is meanwhile exploring Akram's love life. 'I have an English girlfriend,' he says, turning bashfully to include me in the confession. 'But not like Narayan. She lives in Bombay, with her parents. She's a model. Really beautiful. After I make good success, I like to marry her.'

'Have you warned her about the laundry?' Elektra teases, but Akram has more serious things on his mind.

'Her parents don't know yet,' he tells us. 'Nor mine.'

'And she's non-Muslim?' I prompt.

'No, she's Muslim. That part is fine. But her family is rich. That's why I need business success.' Suddenly his eyes are ablaze with the energy to attempt something new. 'I'm planning to start a travel agency, go to Delhi… With Mohamd and Tanu, like three musketeers… We could all rent one room. I tell them, we have to work hard, live simply, not expect any big money for one, two years. Slowly, slowly we grow. Only thing is…' He sounds suddenly less dynamic. 'Mohamd need big money now.'

'Are you sure you want to do this with the others?' I ask. 'They'll drag you down.'

'I promised,' he explains. 'I tell Mumda, any new business, always I bring him in. It's my duty. After all he do for me. Once he tell me, more than all his family, he care for me.'

At last, as I hear that phrase, I understand why the smile is familiar. 'You're Pepsi, aren't you? The boy in the photograph, the one he kept in his pocket?'

He nods shyly. 'I can't let him down.'

'Zzzzlike my younger brother...' grunts the figure to my right, as Akram crosses to speak to Gajendra.

'I was wrong,' says Alex quietly. 'It's Akram you ought to help.'

'It's Akram you *want* to help, isn't it,' says Elektra.

'I've only just met him,' I prevaricate.

'Real potential,' Alex insists. 'Forget Mohamd. Draw a line.'

'Only don't expect too much this time,' says Elektra gently. 'Akram is what he is.'

'I can't let Mohamd down...'

'Listen,' says Alex, rising from his chair, ready to leave, and expecting Elektra to follow suit. 'Nothing you can do for Mohamd will make any difference now. And nothing Akram does will succeed if Mohamd's involved. You win some, you lose some...'

'You're not leaving?' asks Gajendra, seeing my friends on their feet.

'Tell Patrick what you just told me,' Alex bids him and he glances uncomfortably from me to Alex and back again.

'Sir, Mohamd is my very good friend, but like I told you before, he is also lazy. It's hard for me to say this, but once... all those years back, everything was very fine... we thought he was free, free to go to England, free to succeed...'

'Free to fail,' says Alex with satisfaction.

'Free to be forced into marriage,' adds Elektra coldly. 'Patrick said it was always you that insisted he'd no choice.'

Gajendra squirms for a second, but recovers. 'Sir, Madam,

only this I can say. Once, maybe he had a chance… a chance to change…'

'And now?' I press, fearing the answer.

'Now, sir?…' He hesitates for what seems an age. 'Now, I think we should put him in a rickshaw.'

NOW

Fourteen

'Amazing!' says Elektra, as her Blackberry pings again. Since Alex left her, she's been our most regular visitor here in France. She says it's therapeutic: we're the only non-broken home she knows; yet, as Andrew said this morning, she spends so much time on Facebook, she might as well be anywhere. 'Who do you think's just sent a Friend's Request?'

'Your son,' I guess facetiously, looking up from my own computer work. 'An oedipal urge to share snaps of the San Francisco gay scene?'

'I'm keeping tabs on him already,' she laughs. 'That's partly why I joined this thing. If he's still posting pics of his bad behaviour, at least I know he's alive. No, this is from the dipso...' I run my mind quickly through the handful of heavy drinkers in my acquaintance. 'You know, your protégé... Mohamd the Wonderboy! Oh, but look, the poor thing, he's only got nineteen friends, most of them Spanish and the rest called Singh. I suppose I'd better say "yes". My good deed for the day. But, hang on, that's *you* in there; you're in his Friends List! I thought you disapproved of Facebook!'

'I joined when I was organising that university reunion – to help me find people.'

'I'd better add you to my own list. You'll get an email any minute. So, let's see now, who do I know in *your* list? Hardly a soul! I mean, half your own friends are Singhs, or something

Indian!' My laptop bleeps and, to humour Elektra, I confirm that, yes, the woman sharing our home is indeed my friend. 'Oh, but this one's familiar: Gajendra, the one with the restaurant. How's he?'

'Fine, I think. "Very fine", as he would say. He's got a son now, as well as the daughter, so he's happy, like any Indian father. And doing good business, to judge by the photos of his family holidays. He rings us on our mobiles from time to time – mostly at two in the morning, Jaisalmer time, when he's showing off to his pals!'

'I liked Gajendra,' says Elektra. 'But then, so did my evil husband, so I may be mistaken. He's probably forgotten me,' she says, falsely modest. 'But I'll send him a Request. I need all the friends I can get, as an aged "spare woman"! But where's the cute one, the one with the smile... What was he called?'

'You mean Akram?

'Yes, do you hear from him?'

'I do, but not on there. He promised to keep an eye on Mohamd, send me bulletins; and he's been wonderfully dutiful with his emails... But would you believe, he's in Barcelona now, for three months, with a Spanish girlfriend. Goodness knows how he got the visa! They've set up their own little travel agency, mainly for the Spanish market, and they're visiting her parents to drum up business. Then they'll both return to Rajasthan, hoping his own parents will let them marry.'

'So, how much have you invested in that little enterprise?' asks Elektra suspiciously.

'Nothing. He's never so much as hinted. All I've done is help with an English translation for their website. I was hoping we could meet, but his time must almost be up. The last I heard, he was hating the Spanish winter!'

'But loving the Spanish girlfriend,' says Elektra mock-wistfully.

'Anyway, he's *done* something with his life. He didn't let your hero drag him down.'

'You're sounding like Alex.'

'Oh dear, anything but that,' she laughs, then turns serious. 'It's just that you haven't talked about Mohamd for... I don't know, ages... years, in fact... not since we finished that trip. I thought you'd lost touch, written him off.'

'It was more complicated than that. About four months after I got back, he sent an email. I saved it in a folder somewhere... Yes, look.' I hand her the laptop, to read for herself:

'Dear friends hello. hope everythig is fine there? there is no news from your side since long time. i think you are steel angry with me???? please can't you forgive me as you have done all the time... i have decided to live in delhi all the season and i will work from here only. i think this is the only way i can save some money and be on good line. well i have changed little bit. i gave up drinking in day time. i am taking good care of family. when i am in jaisalmer i always go home. hope to hear soon from your side...'

'We should have talked about this before,' says Elektra quietly. 'So, how did you respond?'

'I looked the other day, but I can't seem to find my reply. Perhaps I felt bad about it and deleted it.'

'More denial,' Elektra teases.

'It doesn't matter, I remember pretty clearly... I didn't make it easy for him. I told him it wasn't a question of anger or forgiveness. I still cared about him. I still wanted to help. But I tried to make him understand, there were times when you have to say harsh words, even to someone you love, just like fathers with their sons.'

'But he was making progress...'

'I know. I told him I was pleased he'd turned the corner. It was a start... But it wasn't enough. I said I couldn't help him till he helped himself. It wasn't enough just to give up the daytime drinking and still be half-insensible at night, which was pretty much the message I was getting from Akram. His only hope was to stop altogether.'

'And what did he say?'

'Nothing. Total silence for four or five years. I sent several more messages, but he never replied. It's only thanks to Akram that I know he's got a son! I wrote to congratulate him, but still nothing.'

'Until Facebook?'

'Yes, I invited him to join. And it's funny – somehow the silly superficiality of the thing seems to have made it easier. Broken the ice. He's promised to put some photos of his children on his profile but, like he always said, he's "little bit lazy".'

'His own pics are extraordinary!' says Elektra, still balancing my laptop, but scrolling through Facebook on her own device. 'So much *older*-looking. Middle-aged!'

'He's thirty-two. But Rajasthan does that to you.'

'And the drinking?'

'I'm plucking up courage to ask. Fatherly censure doesn't seem quite the form on Facebook!'

'Well, I'm glad you're back in touch,' says Elektra sincerely. 'This needed resolution.' She's about to hand me back my laptop, when it bleeps again with another new email. 'Who's Nishad?' she asks, unashamedly direct. 'Here, you read it. I won't pry... But I bet you don't look this pleased when one of *my* emails arrives!'

'He's someone we met in Kerala...'

'Oh, yeah,' says Elektra, meaning, 'When have I heard this before?'

'He worked in our hotel,' I explain, undeterred. 'Andrew was spoiling me: we had one of their rooms with a tiny private pool and it was Nishad who came to clean it everyday. So, we chatted with him...'

'Like you do,' Elektra teases.

'We got to know him a bit, asked him what he hoped to do with his life...'

'You never learn, do you?' she laughs.

'I think he'll be different,' I insist. 'For one thing, he's Muslim. The real thing. So definitely no drink. And he's bright. We've spoken to his old teacher who agrees. Would you believe, these days, he needed a diploma, just to clean a swimming pool! Anyway, we're financing a three year correspondence course for a hotel management degree. It's the only way he can get a better job. It'll be tough, all that study at the end of a long working day, but the teacher thinks he can do it.'

'Wouldn't a proper course be better?'

'It's too expensive. And anyway, his parents need the wages from his current job. His father's a rickshaw driver, earning practically nothing.'

'OK, but remember, it's the father... the *real* father who calls the shots here.'

'I know that. But this time the father's totally onside.'

'And another thing... children seldom turn out the way we hope. Look at mine.'

'I know that too. I really care about this boy... Well, you know that, you saw it when the email came in. But believe me, this time I'm ready to be disappointed. I *have* learned *a little*. I *have* changed *a bit*. At the end of the day, Nishad's *free*.'

'Free to let you down?'

'If necessary, yes... He's free to fail.'

Author's Note

When I left the law in 1997 I had no ambitions to be a writer. It didn't even feature on a 'long list' of possible second careers.

However, the decision I had taken, the tearing up one career to 'start again from zero', did feel mildly momentous – made all the more so because I was about to spend a whole winter in a distant country that I had fallen in love with but, as yet, scarcely knew. It therefore seemed important to keep a record of the experience, the better both to remember and to understand it. So I wrote a journal. Mainly for my own benefit, but also for my partner, Andrew, and other friends. If I came back a different person, the diary might at least explain how it had happened.

In the end, I did return determined to write a book, but it wasn't this one. I wanted to produce a work about the Rajasthan Palace Hotels. Factual. Impersonal. And needing research that could justify another long spell in India... But the journal contained what my friends believed was a powerful personal story that ought to be told: the story of Mohamd and Opie and its ironic counterpoint to my own.

I was persuaded to put the palace book aside and turn the journal into a book, which I did and, after a while, I found an agent, Mandy Little, who liked it enough to take me on. It drifted in and out of publishers' offices until John Murray said they weren't sure really about the manuscript (I'm not surprised: as it then stood, it was a pretty naive) but they liked the way I wrote, so what else might I like to write about? And by this time I was already established in the Languedoc and all fired up about the wine revolution happening there, so I ended up writing *Virgile's Vineyard* and its food-focused sequel *Arrazat's Aubergines*.

Meanwhile, the Mohamd story had moved on. Or rather, it had gone badly wrong and the need to tell it seemed all the more important. The book is divided into two sections: 'Before' and 'After'. And what happened in between was that Mohamd was obliged to go through with an unsuitable marriage that had been planned for him by his family.

I hope that the book has made clear that I have absolutely no quarrel with arranged marriages as such. I have seen huge numbers of them work very well, far better than many made freely from choice in our own society. But Mohamd's was a case where he had already changed himself too much, taken his way of life too far outside the traditions of his community for the conventional approach to end happily. So many people have said to me, 'But surely, he could always say "no"?' Ever since all this happened, I have wanted to explain to a world that has never heard of Mohamd why he couldn't and didn't. And why that led to disaster.

In telling this tale, I have 'juggled' very slightly with a few of the personalities and locations, as well as adjusting certain time scales, but all of the incidents and characters described are based on real, often painfully real, experience. However, as Philip Pullman once helpfully observed to me, 'You're not in a court of law any longer. You're writing a book, not an affidavit.' I merely hope that all those who appear in this story will understand.

Above all, I hope that Mohamd will forgive the fact that this book gives more prominence to his unhappy life than he may have imagined when he told me that day in the desert, '*You should write one more book. Tell people all what happen here. Make them understand.*' I hope he will also forgive me for never managing to help him more meaningfully, in the way I had hoped. The least that I can do is to dedicate the book to him – with love and, yes, for all that went awry, continuing heartfelt admiration.

Acknowledgements

There are many – too numerous to catalogue here – who have assisted and encouraged me in the writing of this book and I hope they will forgive me, if I single out but a few: Emma Bradford and Neil Philip for helping me to grasp what it was really about; Lynne Suo for helping me face up to what was wrong with it and for all manner of other assistance; and Andrew McKenzie, as always, for unfailing support in all things.

Also by Patrick Moon

VIRGILE'S VINEYARD
A Year in the Languedoc Wine Country

In his first book, Patrick Moon explores the world of Languedoc wine. He sets out to discover how a region, so long notorious for mere quantity, has managed to transform itself, in little more than a decade, into one of the world's most exciting vineyards.

Among the rich cast of characters he meets during his year of exploration is Virgile, a young local wine-maker who offers to initiate Patrick into the mysteries of each season's work in the fields and in the cellar. Virgile is passionately committed to perfection, though he operates on a shoestring, with only a handful of hectares and the smallest cellar imaginable.

At the other extreme is Manu, Patrick's dipsomaniac neighbour, a diehard traditionalist producing a private wine-lake of unspeakable *rouge*. With Manu as his self-appointed guide, Patrick embarks on a quest for the revolution's leading lights – a succession of lively encounters with growers as varied as the wines themselves, from modest one-man bands to the owners of elegant chateaux, with every approach from the very latest in mechanised efficiency to old-fashioned eccentricity,

Interwoven with these bucolic expeditions are digressions into the history of the region and its wine-making, from earliest plantings by the Greeks and Romans to the nineteenth-century scourge of phylloxera.

Meanwhile the author struggles to deal with his remote and long-neglected French home – an unfamiliar and unpredictable world where the brambles have grown as tall as the olive trees, the water supply has just dried up and there is a ferocious animal under the roof tiles.

'Patrick Moon writes with flair... A fascinating seasonal tour'
DAILY MAIL

'Unlike the usual enthusiastic refugees from the north, Moon conducts himself with a mixture of surprise and reluctance. Like the wine, everything flows richly and generously from there'
SUNDAY TIMES

'Rather superior and enjoyably informative... Moon conveys a host of information about this fascinating corner of France and its main product' *INDEPENDENT*

'Full of interesting characters and a fresh view of a fast-evolving region from an outsider who loves wine and is prepared to learn why one bottle, vineyard or estate differs so dramatically from another' *WINE MAGAZINE*

'A crash course in wine-making and a hilarious introduction to French hospitality... The story is in turns funny, moving and instructional, with a wisdom that rises from every chapter and glassful. A delightful journey of calamity and discovery'
GOOD BOOK GUIDE

'Humane, funny and quirky... The perfect antidote to Peter Mayle'
PAUL LEVY

'Funny and involving... Moon's witty banter flows as readily as the wine' *EVERYTHING FRANCE*

'Beautifully written... can just as easily be savoured by teetotallers as by wine fanatics' *JANCIS ROBINSON*

'Entertaining' *THE WEEK*

'Good fun if you don't drink, even more fun if you do'
FOCUS MAGAZINE

'I became totally absorbed by its light-hearted insight into winemaking in the emerging Languedoc region... A thoroughly enjoyable read, I found it an entertaining way to become an authority on the Languedoc without leaving my armchair' *BIRMINGHAM EVENING POST*

'This is a book for anyone who appreciates wine and is interested in learning more about one of France's most colourful and historic regions' *THE GLOBE AND MAIL*

'Sit back and quaff this tale that's part wine guide, part travelogue and wholly enjoyable... It's a glorious romp in which the reader may both learn something about the area of southern France and even pick up a few wine-making tips along the way. Eat your heart out Peter Mayle' *WORCESTER EVENING NEWS*

ARRAZAT'S AUBERGINES
Inside a Languedoc Kitchen

In his sequel to *Virgile's Vineyard*, Patrick Moon explores the world of Languedoc food and *cuisine*.

Returning to his challenging home, he could easily have filled the days, protecting infant vines from marauding wild boar and hiding baby truffle oaks from unscrupulous neighbours. However, the local campsite café is now an ambitious new restaurant and the determination of its talented young chef to achieve perfection on a shoestring is intriguing. Patrick soon finds himself with sleeves rolled up, pitching in to share for a year the triumphs, disasters and sheer hard work of life in a serious kitchen. But will the VIP diners guess that he has never made mayonnaise before? Or that he put the wrong sauce on the starter?...

A wider exploration of the region's finest produce for the table distracts him further. From season to season, Patrick's quest uncovers the secrets of olive oil and salt production, the mysteries of Ricard and the Roquefort caves, the miracle of the sparkling Perrier spring. From mighty household names to eccentric peasant smallholdings, his expeditions encompass an extraordinary cast of characters and a rich vein of humour.

But always there are the vines and olives, not to mention aubergines, demanding attention at home.

Arrazat's Aubergines is a great read for any Francophile or food-lover and, for fans of *Virgile's Vineyard,* it continues Patrick's adventures with Manu and other familiar characters, whilst also following the continuing progress of Virgile himself.

'The perfect food-based sequel to his wine book' *RESTAURANT MAGAZINE*

'Enough erudition and warmth to make it as rewarding as one of the sensational local Roqueforts... Moon finds himself immersed in the back-breaking but romantic business of Languedoc cuisine, and leads us on a mouth-watering odyssey through snails, crayfish, foie gras – and aubergines. The humour is gentle but this is a thoughtful – and by no means misty-eyed – paean to the people and food of the region.' *DAILY MAIL*

'The buffet of colourful characters and food adventures will please Francophiles, foodies and anyone who wants to experience *la vie rustique*—without the hassles of actually living it.' *PUBLISHERS WEEKLY*

'His drive, affection and enthusiasm for his subject matter shine through' *IN-HOUSE LAWYER*

'Cleverly combines the slog of *Hell's Kitchen* with all the familiar, friendly elements of foreign fantasy.' *THE TIMES*

★

Visit: www.patrickmoon.co.uk